# CLASSICS *for* YOUNG READERS

Volume 7

Editor: John Holdren

Art Director: Steve Godwin

Designer: Jayoung Cho

Illustrators:
Jayoung Cho
Gail McIntosh
Deborah Wolfe Ltd. (Jerry Dadds, Jim Hays, Rob Kemp, Jeff LeVan, Dan
McGeehan, Graham Parslow, Anton Petrov, Phillip Small)

ISBN: 1-931728-52-6

# TABLE OF CONTENTS

## THE HEART'S DEEP CORE

## STORIES FROM THE BIBLE

## STORIES IN VERSE
## NARRATIVE POEMS

# Stories of Scientists

# Irony

# Favorites from Famous Books
## A Christmas Carol

# Life Stories

# WHAT'S IMPORTANT

# THE LANGUAGE OF POETRY

# ADVICE AND INSTRUCTION

# THE HEART'S
# DEEP CORE

# Chura and Marwe

*an African folktale as told by Humphrey Harman*

$F$ar to the east there is a great mountain, whose top is lacquered with silver every month of the year. Upon the slopes of this once lived a boy and a girl. He was called Chura and she Marwe and they were slave children, got cheap and kept by a household of the Chagga people to watch crops and herd goats.

Now Chura had a face like a toad's and Marwe was so beautiful that when people saw them together they exclaimed, "Eh! How is it that God could make two so different?"

That, however, was not how Marwe saw it. Chura was her companion and the only one she had. They loved each other dearly, were happy together and only when they were together, for they had little else to be happy about.

One day they were sent to watch a field and keep the monkeys from eating the beans. The place was on the lower slopes of the mountain, a clearing in the forest, and there all day the children sat beating a pot with a stick whenever they heard a monkey chatter thievishly behind the wall of leaves. Hemmed in with tall trees, the field was airless and hot, and by late afternoon they could stand their thirst no longer. They slipped off to where a stream, cold from the snows above, fell noisily down a cliff into a pool. The water there was deep and upon its dark surface one leaf floated in a circle all day.

---

lacquered: coated with a glossy finish
thievishly: in a thief-like way; sneakily
hemmed in: surrounded by

Here they drank hastily, washed the tiredness from their faces, then ran back to the field. Alas, in the little time they had been away the monkeys had stripped it.

Marwe wept and Chura stared at the plundered bean plants with a bleak face. The folk they worked for were harsh and the children knew they would be beaten. Chura tried to comfort his friend, but there was little of that he could give her and at last, in despair, she ran into the forest. Chura followed, calling for her to stop, and was just in time to see her throw herself into the pool where, at once, she sank from sight.

Chura could not swim and he knew the pool to be deep. He ran round the edge calling, but it was no use. The dark water quietened, the leaf again circled placidly, and Marwe was gone.

Chura went back to the household and told those who owned him of the loss of Marwe and the crop. They followed him to the pool, where nothing was to be seen, and then to the field, where the sight of ruined plants made them angry. They beat Chura, and some days later, grieving for Marwe and tired of ill-treatment, he ran away and the Chagga never saw him again.

Soon another pair of children watched the crops or herded goats, and whether they found life better than Chura and Marwe had is unknown.

When Marwe flung herself into the pool she sank slowly through water which changed from bright light of noon to

---

plundered: stolen; taken by force
bleak: gloomy; without hope
placidly: calmly

the deep blue of late evening and finally to the darkness of a night with neither moon nor stars. And there she stepped out into the Underworld, shook water from her hair and wandered, chilled to the heart by the grayness of the place.

Presently she came to a hut on the slope of a hill, with an old woman outside preparing supper for the small children playing on the swept earth at her feet. Beyond the hut, just where the hill curved over and away, was a village that seemed as if it had just been built, for the logs of the stockade were white as if the bark had been stripped from them that day and the thatch of the houses was new-dried and trim.

The old woman asked Marwe where she was going, and Marwe replied timidly that she was a stranger and alone and wanted to go to the village she saw above, to ask for food and perhaps work so that she could live her life.

"It's not yet time to go there," said the woman. "Stay with me and work here. You'll not go hungry or lack a place by the fire if you do so."

So Marwe accepted this offer and lived with the old woman. She cared for the children, fetched water from the stream, and weeded a garden. Her new mistress was kind and so life for Marwe went on without hardship.

Only sometimes she pined for the sunlight and birdsong of the world above, for here it was never anything but gray. And always she longed for Chura.

And now let us follow what happened to him.

He drifted from village to village of the Chagga, asking for food and work but, because of his ugliness, no one would take him in. Food they offered hastily and then they told him

stockade. a line of posts surrounding a village
pined: yearned; longed for

uneasily to go. It seemed to men and even more to women that such an ill-favored face must have been earned by great evil and could only bring with it worse luck. So, wandering from hamlet to village, gradually inching his way round the mountain, he was fed by unwilling charity or, more often, by what small game he could kill or field he could rob. As the years passed he grew strong and hard but no better looking.

One day he left the forest and the tall grass of the foothills and walked north into the sun-bitten plain. Here the trees were bleached and shrunken, standing wide apart, their thin leaves throwing little shade. Between them the ants built red towers and covered every dead leaf or stick with a crust of dry earth.

A juiceless land where grass was scarce and water more so, and here lived the Masai.

They are a people who greatly love three things: children, cattle, and war. Standing like storks upon one leg, holding spears with blades long as an arm, and shields blazing with color, they guarded their cattle and looked with amused indifference upon the lives of other men.

They found Chura wandering and thirsty, carelessly decided not to kill him, and made him a servant. At his ugliness they only laughed.

"What's it to us if you look like a toad?" they shouted. "All men other than Masai are animals anyway. And usually look like them."

So Chura milked cows, mended cattle fences, and made himself useful until one night a lion attacked the calves. Then he took a spear from a hut and went out and killed it.

---

hamlet: a small town or village
indifference: the state of being unconcerned, of not caring one way
   or another

"Wah!" said the Masai when they came running and found Chura with the great beast dead at his feet. "Alone and without a shield! This is a new light you show yourself in. Well, you weren't born Masai, though plainly some mistake's been made by the gods over that. Somewhere within you there must be a Masai of sorts, otherwise you couldn't have done this. We'll accept you for one."

So they gave him the spear he had borrowed, and a shield whose weight made him stagger. When the lion's skin had been cured they made from it a headdress that framed Chura's face in a circle of long tawny hair and added two feet to his height.

"There, now you look almost human," they said. "Only something must be done about that name of yours. It means *toad* and no Masai could live with it."

"Well then, what am I to be called?" asked Chura.

"Hm. Punda Malia (Donkey)?" suggested one.

"No, no, Kifaru (Rhino)," said another.

"What about Nguruwe (Pig)?" threw in another.

"If you can't be civil…" began Chura, taking a firm grip on his spear.

"Heh! Keep your temper, Brother. We mean no harm. Now, what can your name be?"

They spent a happy evening making suggestions and falling about with laughter at their own wit. But finally they pulled themselves together and found for Chura a name which seemed to them far more suitable than the one he had brought with him.

When Marwe had lived for a number of years in the Underworld and grown to be as beautiful a woman as she

civil: polite; courteous

had been a child, she became homesick. The old woman noticed her sadness and asked what caused it. Marwe hesitated, because she did not want to seem ungrateful for the kindness that had been given to her but, in the end, she said that she pined to go back to her own world. The old woman was not offended.

"Ah," she said, "then it's time you went to the village. In this matter I can't help, but they may."

Next day Marwe climbed the hill and waited at the village gate. When she had sat there for some time a number of old men came out. They were dressed in cotton robes that shone through the gloom about, and they greeted her and asked what she wanted. Marwe replied that she wished to return to the world above.

"Hm," they said. "We'll see, yes, we'll see."

Then one who seemed the most important among them asked, "Child, which would you sooner have, the warm or the cold?"

The question bewildered Marwe. "I don't understand," she replied.

Shadows seemed to cross their faces and their voices grew fainter. "That's nothing to us," they said. "You've heard our question and we can do nothing unless you answer. Which would you prefer, the warm or the cold?"

Marwe understood that this was a test which it must be important for her to consider with care.

"Warmth ... or cold?" she pondered. "Well, everyone would sooner have warmth than cold because cold is bitter and difficult to endure, while warmth is life itself. Yet surely their riddle can't be as easy as that."

When she had thought again, as deeply as she could, it seemed that if the choice was between what is usually thought to be good and bad, her life pointed the other way.

"For," said she, "Chura was ugly and unwanted, yet he was kind and I loved him. And the Underworld is feared by everyone, yet here I've met greater kindness than I ever knew in the sunlit world above."

And she made up her mind and said, "No matter what others believe, I'll trust my own wisdom and choose the cold."

The old men listened to her answer with faces from which she could read nothing, and they offered her two pots. From the mouth of one rose steam, while the other sent out a chill that struck to the bone of a hand brought near it.

"Choose as you've chosen," they urged her and so, faithful to her own belief, she dipped a hand into the cold pot and brought it out covered to the elbow with richly-made bracelets.

"Don't hesitate to take more," they urged her. "Neither we nor the pots will be offended."

So she reached in her other arm and in turn both her feet, and came out heavy with bangles and anklets, heavy precious things made from copper and gold, ornaments worth more than the tribute of a whole tribe.

The old men smiled and told her that she had chosen well and been wise. And still they loaded her with treasures, necklaces of shell, rings, and eardrops. They brought her a fine kilt worked all over with gold wire and beads that glowed blue as the skies she remembered from the world above.

"Now," they said, "we've one more gift: a piece of advice. When you are back in your own world you'll wish in time to

---

tribute: a payment, usually from one ruler or nation to another, for
    protection or service
kilt: a knee-length skirt

marry and there'll be no shortage of those who'll ask for you. Go softly, don't hasten. Wait for someone with the name of Simba to ask, and choose him."

Then, gathering their robes clear of their feet, the old ones led her to the pool. Gently they urged her in and she rose like a thought until she broke the sunlit surface, where the leaf still circled and birds sang in the trees about.

She left the water, sat upon the bank with the light dancing on her finery, and waited for the world to find her.

And very soon it did.

News spread that beside a pool in the forest sat a woman, rich and of amazing beauty, waiting for a husband. They flocked to her with offers, handsome young men, rich landowners, daring hunters, great warriors, even powerful chiefs. And all singing much the same tune, "Here's fame or wealth or power or glory or beauty or… if only you'll marry me!"

She pointed at each one of them the same sharp little question, "What's your name?"

"Name! Why, it's Nyati or Mamba or Tembo or Ndovu or…" and so on. No end of names and at all she shook her head and replied, "I'm sorry, but that will not be the name of my husband."

Now the news flew even as far as the plain, down where the cattle trudge through the dust, the lion hunts, and the vulture sits upon the thorn. At last it reached Chura, and at once he took spear and shield and came tirelessly running and his heart singing, "Marwe's back from the Underworld and I'll see her!"

---

finery: fancy clothing and jewelry

When he came to where she sat beside her pool and cried "Marwe!" she recognized his ugliness even framed as it was by a lion's mane. Part of her laughed and the rest wept.

"Oh, Chura," she cried. "Why is life so unkind? I shall never love anyone but you, yet my fate says that we can't marry."

"Then who can you marry?" he demanded.

"Only a man named Simba."

"But that's my name," he roared. "Simba! Lion! The Masai named me that when I killed a lion."

So, of course, they were married. What was there to stop them? It would have been striking fate across the face not to marry. But everyone marveled that so beautiful a woman should choose so ugly a husband.

They paid no attention to them and—it's a strange thing and scarcely to be believed—but, do you know, the moment they were married something happened to his ugly toad's face and he became good to look at.

Well, passable.

So they say.

I don't imagine for one moment that Marwe cared either way.

# THE TIGER'S WHISKER
*a Korean folktale as told by Harold Courlander*

**A** young woman by the name of Yun Ok came one day to
the house of a mountain hermit to seek his help. The hermit
was a sage of great renown and a maker of charms and
magic potions.

When Yun Ok entered his house, the hermit said, without
raising his eyes from the fireplace into which he was looking,
"Why are you here?"

Yun Ok said, "Oh, Famous Sage, I am in distress! Make
me a potion!"

"Yes, yes, make a potion! Everyone needs potions! Can we
cure a sick world with a potion?"

"Master," Yun Ok replied, "if you do not help me, I am
truly lost!"

"Well, what is your story?" the hermit said, resigned at
last to listen.

"It is my husband," Yun Ok said. "He is very dear to me.
For the past three years he has been away fighting in the
wars. Now that he has returned, he hardly speaks to me, or
to anyone else. If I speak, he doesn't seem to hear. When he
talks at all, it is roughly. If I serve him food not to his liking,
he pushes it aside and angrily leaves the room. Sometimes
when he should be working in the rice field, I see him sitting
idly on top of the hill, looking toward the sea."

---

hermit: one who lives alone and apart from society
sage: a wise person
renown: fame
resigned: having accepted or submitted to something

"Yes, so it is sometimes when young men come back from the wars," the hermit said. "Go on."

"There is no more to tell, Learned One. I want a potion to give my husband so that he will be loving and gentle, as he used to be."

"Ha, so simple, is it?" the hermit said. "A potion! Very well; come back in three days and I will tell you what we shall need for such a potion."

Three days later Yun Ok returned to the home of the mountain sage. "I have looked into it," he told her. "Your potion can be made. But the most essential ingredient is the whisker of a living tiger. Bring me this whisker and I will give you what you need."

"The whisker of a living tiger!" Yun Ok said. "How could I possibly get it?"

"If the potion is important enough, you will succeed," the hermit said. He turned his head away, not wishing to talk any more.

Yun Ok went home. She thought a great deal about how she would get the tiger's whisker. Then one night when her husband was asleep, she crept from her house with a bowl of rice and meat sauce in her hand. She went to the place on the mountainside where the tiger was known to live. Standing far off from the tiger's cave, she held out the bowl of food, calling the tiger to come and eat. The tiger did not come.

The next night Yun Ok went again, this time a little bit closer. Again she offered a bowl of food. Every night Yun Ok went to the mountain, each time a few steps nearer the tiger's cave than the night before. Little by little the tiger became accustomed to seeing her there.

One night Yun Ok approached to within a stone's throw of the tiger's cave. This time the tiger came a few steps toward her and stopped. The two of them stood looking at one another in the moonlight. It happened again the following night, and this time they were so close that Yun Ok could talk to the tiger in a soft, soothing voice. The next night, after looking carefully into Yun Ok's eyes, the tiger ate the food that she held out for him. After that when Yun Ok came in the night, she found the tiger waiting for her on the trail. When the tiger had eaten, Yun Ok could gently rub his head with her hand. Nearly six months had passed since the night of her first visit. At last one night, after caressing the animal's head, Yun Ok said:

"Oh, Tiger, generous animal, I must have one of your whiskers. Do not be angry with me!"

And she snipped off one of the whiskers.

The tiger did not become angry, as she had feared he might. Yun Ok went down the trail, not walking but running, with the whisker clutched tightly in her hand.

The next morning she was at the mountain hermit's house just as the sun was rising from the sea. "Oh, Famous One!" she cried, "I have it! I have the tiger's whisker! Now you can make me the potion you promised so that my husband will be loving and gentle again!"

The hermit took the whisker and examined it. Satisfied that it had really come from a tiger, he leaned forward and dropped it into the fire that burned in his fireplace.

"Oh, sir!" the young woman called in anguish. "What have you done with it!"

"Tell me how you obtained it," the hermit said.

---

caressing: gently rubbing
anguish: extreme physical or mental pain

"Why, I went to the mountain each night with a little bowl of food. At first I stood afar, and I came a little closer each time, gaining the tiger's confidence. I spoke gently and soothingly to him, to make him understand I wished him only good. I was patient. Each night I brought him food, knowing that he would not eat. But I did not give up. I came again and again. I never spoke harshly. I never reproached him. And at last one night he took a few steps toward me. A time came when he would meet me on the trail and eat out of the bowl that I held in my hands. I rubbed his head, and he made happy sounds in his throat. Only after that did I take the whisker."

"Yes, yes," the hermit said, "you tamed the tiger and won his confidence and love."

"But you have thrown the whisker in the fire!" Yun Ok cried. "It is all for nothing!"

"No, I do not think it is all for nothing," the hermit said. "The whisker is no longer needed. Yun Ok, let me ask you, is a man more vicious than a tiger? Is he less responsive to kindness and understanding? If you can win the love and confidence of a wild and bloodthirsty animal by gentleness and patience, surely you can do the same with your husband?"

Hearing this, Yun Ok stood speechless for a moment. Then she went down the trail, turning over in her mind the truth she had learned in the house of the mountain hermit.

---

reproached: blamed; criticized harshly

# Stopping by Woods on a Snowy Evening

*by Robert Frost*

Whose woods these are I think I know.
His house is in the village, though;
He will not see me stopping here
To watch his woods fill up with snow.

My little horse must think it queer
To stop without a farmhouse near
Between the woods and frozen lake
The darkest evening of the year.

He gives his harness bells a shake
To ask if there is some mistake.
The only other sound's the sweep
Of easy wind and downy flake.

The woods are lovely, dark, and deep.
But I have promises to keep,
And miles to go before I sleep,
And miles to go before I sleep.

# THE STORY OF SCARFACE

*a Blackfoot Indian legend*
*adapted from a retelling by Amy Cruse*

Among the people called the Blackfoot, there once lived an orphan boy who had no friends to take care of him. The women of the tribe helped him as well as they could, giving him what they could spare of food and clothing. The men took him on their hunting expeditions, and taught him just as they taught their own sons. The boy grew up strong and brave, and the men of the tribe said that one day he would make a mighty hunter.

On one of these hunting expeditions, the boy met a great grizzly bear and fought a desperate fight with him. During the struggle the bear raked its sharp claws across the boy's face. When the wound healed, the boy's face was marked by an ugly red scar. From this time, he was called Scarface.

Scarface had a brave heart, and he thought little of his disfigured face—until, that is, he fell in love with the daughter of the chief of his tribe.

Every young man in the tribe wished to wed the beautiful daughter of the chief. They put on their finest warrior's garb and boasted of their brave deeds, but she did not care for their finery or their bold talk. As each ventured to ask for her hand in marriage, she refused them all.

As for Scarface, he did not even dare to approach her. Though he loved her, he remained silent, and his heart ached whenever he thought of the terrible scar on his face. He did

---

garb: clothing

not know that the girl thought he was braver and truer than the other young men who boldly sought her affection.

One day, as she sat outside her father's lodge, Scarface passed by, and as he passed he looked at her. His eyes could not hide his love and admiration. A young warrior whom the girl had refused noticed the look, and said with a sneer, "See here, Scarface has become a suitor for our chief's daughter. Go on, Scarface—approach her! Since she will have nothing to do with men whose faces are unmarked, perhaps she will choose you, ugly as you are."

Scarface felt hot anger rise within him. Looking very steadily at the young man, he said, "My brother speaks true words, though he speaks with an ill tongue. I will indeed ask the daughter of our great chief to be my wife."

The young man laughed loudly in mockery. Other young men of the tribe came up, and they also laughed, and pretended to bow down before Scarface. He took no notice, but walked away quietly, though in his heart he yearned to spring at them as the great grizzly had sprung at him in the forest.

He came to the river, where the chief's daughter had gone to gather rushes for the basket she was weaving. When he saw her, his anger died away. He drew near to her, knowing that if he did not speak at once, his courage would leave him.

"I have no wealth or pemmican, as the great warriors of the tribe have," he said. "I live by my bow and spear. And my face is terribly marred. Yet I love you. Will you dwell in my lodge and be my wife?"

suitor: a man who courts a woman with the hope of marrying her
mockery: ridicule; insulting, scornful speech or action
pemmican: a Native American food made of dried meat and fruit
   in small cakes
marred: damaged; harmed

"That you are poor," she replied, "does not matter, for my father has great wealth that he would give me upon my marriage. But I may not be your bride. The great lord of the Sun has commanded me not to marry."

When Scarface heard these words, his heart sank. Yet he did not give up hope. "Perhaps the lord of the Sun will take back his command. He is kind and gives many good gifts."

"Go to him, then," said the girl. "Ask him to release me from his command. And, so that I may know he has done so, ask him to take the scar from your face as a sign."

"I will go and do as you say," said Scarface. And he turned and started on his journey.

He traveled for many miles, through the forest and over mountains, across rivers and glowing prairies, but met no one who could help him find the way to the country of the Sun. At last he came to a lodge on the edge of the golden prairie, where he found an old woman sitting on the doorstep.

"Can you tell me," he asked, "how I may find the lodge of the Sun?"

"The way is long and hard," she said. But she saw strength in his eyes, so she continued, "I will put you on the path. If your heart does not fail you, you will reach the Sky Country."

The old woman gave him a pair of moccasins and a pouch full of pemmican. "Take these," she said, "and walk to the sea. Sit down on the shore for three days. Then you will know how to reach the dwelling-place of the Sun."

Scarface thanked the old woman, put on the moccasins, carried the pouch of pemmican in one hand, and hastened across the trackless prairie.

He journeyed for months, until he lost count of the days, until his pemmican was gone and his moccasins were worn through. And then, at last, he reached the sea. As the old woman had directed him, he sat down on the shore and waited, and on the third day, when the sun was sinking below the distant edge of the water, he saw a shining trail that led to the Sky Country.

The young man leapt up at once and hurried down the glowing path. Then, as he rounded a bend, he saw a bow and a quiver full of gleaming arrows lying just to the side of the trail. He looked at them in wonder.

"Those must belong to a great hunter," he breathed. "I have never seen any so fine."

But Scarface did not pick them up. "They are beautiful," he thought, "but they are not mine to take."

So he continued down the path. Soon he saw a young man coming toward him. The handsome stranger walked with a sprightly step, and his eyes sparkled, and he even seemed to glow with a soft light.

"I am looking for my bow and arrows," the stranger said to Scarface. "Have you seen them?"

"I just passed them," replied Scarface. "They are lying by the side of the trail not far from here. I will show you."

Scarface brought the young man to where the bow and arrows lay. As the youth picked them up, he smiled and said, "I thought it unfortunate to have lost my bow and arrows. But now I think I am lucky indeed, for not only have I found them, but a friend besides. Tell me, where are you going? Perhaps we can walk a ways together."

"I am trying to reach the Sun's lodge," replied Scarface.

---

quiver: a case for carrying arrows

"It is indeed nearby," said the young man.

"You know where it is?" asked Scarface.

"I do," the youth replied, "for I am Morning Star. The Sun is my father, and his lodge is my home. Come with me, and I will take you there."

But as they walked along the path, Morning Star said, "I warn you, my father is hasty and hot-tempered. He may kill you for having come here." Then he sighed, "We will ask my mother what to do."

When the two young men arrived at the Sun's lodge, Morning Star opened the door, and called to his mother, the Moon. "Mother," he said, "this young man is my friend. He has come from a distant land beyond the waters to see the Sun. Please, let us help him."

The Moon nodded, and when the Sun returned to the lodge in the evening, she pleaded with him to spare Scarface's life. The Sun looked hard at Scarface. His face was so bright that Scarface could not return his gaze, but he stood bravely and did not flinch.

After a few moments, the Sun dimmed his rays and said to Morning Star, "You wish this young man to be your companion?"

"Yes," replied Morning Star. "I am tired of hunting alone."

"Very well," said the Sun. Then, turning to Scarface he said, "Stay with us for a season. You will find good game here. My son, who loves the chase, will go with you."

"I will stay, great lord," replied Scarface.

And so Scarface stayed with the Sun, the Moon, and Morning Star in their lodge in the Sky Country. Each day, the two young men went hunting, for the Sun told them that

---

hasty: acting quickly and often without thought

they could go anywhere they pleased, except to the lair of monstrous birds. "You must not go there," said the Sun. "They will try to kill my son."

But Morning Star yearned to try his skill against the dread birds. So one day, he slipped away from Scarface and crept down to their lair. At once, the flock descended upon him, and they would have torn him to pieces. But Scarface heard their hideous cries and ran to the aid of Morning Star. He dashed in among the fierce creatures and beat them off with his club. Then he seized Morning Star and hurried him back through the forest to safety.

When they returned to the lodge that night, Morning Star told his father of his own disobedience and the courage of Scarface.

"You have saved my son from a dreadful death," said the Sun to Scarface. "How shall I repay you? Ask of me some favor. After all, what was it that brought you here? Surely you had some desire in your heart or you would not have traveled so far and risked such danger."

The kind words of the Sun gave Scarface the courage to speak the thing that had long been on his mind but which he had not dared to ask. "In my own land," he said, "I love a maiden who is the daughter of the chief of my people. But I am only a poor warrior, with a disfigured face that is terrible to see. Still, she in her goodness loves me, and would marry me, but for your command that she will marry no man. O great lord, I came to you to ask that you free her from your command so we might wed and live in happiness together."

"Go back," said the Sun, "and take the maiden for your wife. Tell her it is my will that she marry you. As for the scar on your face—truly, I think you have made a great journey for so small a blemish."

Then he invited both Morning Star and Scarface to sit with him in the sweat-lodge. And when they came out again, the two young men looked alike.

The Sun stood behind the two youths and said to the Moon, "Which one is Morning Star?"

The Moon looked carefully, and pointed to one of them.

"That is Scarface!" laughed the Sun. "From now on, we will call him The-One-You-Took-For-Morning-Star. We will call him Star-face."

"Come," said the Sun to Star-face. "Take this shirt and leggings, and bring them back to your people. Sing the songs I will teach you, so they will know of your great deed."

When Star-face had learned the songs, he said, "Thank you. Now I must return to my people. I am grateful to you, but I have been here long enough." And so he said a fond farewell to Morning Star, the Moon, and the Sun.

Then the Sun sent him back to his tribe. All the people came to look at the richly clad young warrior, who walked with such a quick, light step. But none knew him for Scarface. Even the chief's daughter did not recognize him when she first looked upon him, but a second look told her who he was, and she called his name. But then, realizing that the scar was gone, and understanding what its disappearance meant, she sprang to him with a cry of joy.

The story of his wonderful journey was told, and the chief gladly gave his daughter in marriage to this warrior on whom the great lord of the Sun had looked with favor.

---

sweat-lodge: used in rituals by some Native Americans, a hut or cavern
   in which steam is created by pouring water on hot stones
clad: clothed; covered

# SYMPATHY

*by Paul Laurence Dunbar*

I know what the caged bird feels, alas!
　　When the sun is bright on the upland slopes;
　When the wind stirs soft through the springing grass,
　And the river flows like a stream of glass;
　　When the first bird sings and the first bud opes,
　And the faint perfume from its chalice steals—
　I know what the caged bird feels!

I know why the caged bird beats his wing
　　Till its blood is red on the cruel bars;
　For he must fly back to his perch and cling
　When he fain would be on the bough a-swing;
　　And a pain still throbs in the old, old scars
　And they pulse again with a keener sting—
　I know why he beats his wing!

I know why the caged bird sings, ah me,
　　When his wing is bruised and his bosom sore,—
　When he beats his bars and he would be free;
　It is not a carol of joy or glee,
　　But a prayer that he sends from his heart's deep core,
　But a plea, that upward to Heaven he flings—
　I know why the caged bird sings!

---

opes: poetic form of "opens"　　keener: sharper
chalice: a cup　　bosom: the chest, especially
fain: rather　　　　　when thought of as including
bough: a branch　　　　the heart and emotions

# The Happy Prince

*adapted from the story by Oscar Wilde*

High above the city, on a tall column, stood the statue of the Happy Prince. He was gilded all over with thin leaves of fine gold, for eyes he had two bright sapphires, and a large red ruby glowed on his sword-hilt.

He was very much admired indeed. "Why can't you be like the Happy Prince?" asked a sensible mother of her little boy who was crying for the moon. "The Happy Prince never dreams of crying for anything."

"I am glad there is someone in the world who is quite happy," muttered a disappointed man as he gazed at the wonderful statue.

"He looks just like an angel," said the Charity Children as they came out of the cathedral in their bright scarlet cloaks and their clean white pinafores.

"How do you know?" said the Mathematical Master, "you have never seen one."

"Ah! but we have, in our dreams," answered the children; and the Mathematical Master frowned and looked very severe, for he did not approve of children dreaming.

One night there flew over the city a little Swallow. His friends had gone away to Egypt six weeks before, but he had stayed behind, for he was in love with the most beautiful Reed. He had met her early in the spring as he was flying down the

gilded: covered with a thin layer of gold
hilt: a handle, especially of a sword
pinafores: sleeveless dresses often worn by young girls
reed: a tall, slender stalk of grass

river after a big yellow moth, and had been so attracted by her slender waist that he had stopped to talk to her.

After the other swallows had gone he felt lonely and began to tire of his lady-love. "She has no conversation," he said, "and I am afraid that she is a coquette, for she is always flirting with the wind." And certainly, whenever the wind blew, the Reed made the most graceful curtseys. "I admit that she is domestic," he continued, "but I love traveling, and my wife, consequently, should love traveling also."

"Will you come away with me?" he said finally to her; but the Reed shook her head, she was so attached to her home.

"You have been trifling with me," he cried. "I am off to the Pyramids. Good-bye!" and he flew away.

All day long he flew, and at nighttime he arrived at the city. "Where shall I put up?" he said. "I hope the town has made preparations."

Then he saw the statue on the tall column. "I will put up there," he cried. "It is a fine position, with plenty of fresh air." So he alighted just between the feet of the Happy Prince.

"I have a golden bedroom," he said softly to himself as he looked round, and he prepared to go to sleep. But just as he was putting his head under his wing a large drop of water fell on him.

"What a curious thing!" he cried; "there is not a single cloud in the sky, the stars are quite clear and bright, and yet it is raining. The climate in the north of Europe is really dreadful. The Reed used to like the rain, but that was merely her selfishness."

Then another drop fell.

coquette: a flirt
trifling: toying; fooling
alighted: landed

"What is the use of a statue if it cannot keep the rain off?" he said; "I must look for a good chimney-pot," and he determined to fly away.

But before he had opened his wings, a third drop fell, and he looked up, and saw—Ah! what did he see?

The eyes of the Happy Prince were filled with tears, and tears were running down his golden cheeks. His face was so beautiful in the moonlight that the little Swallow was filled with pity.

"Who are you?" he asked.

"I am the Happy Prince."

"Why are you weeping then?" asked the Swallow. "You have quite drenched me."

"When I was alive and had a human heart," answered the statue, "I did not know what tears were, for I lived in the Palace of Sans-Souci, where sorrow is not allowed to enter. In the daytime I played with my companions in the garden, and in the evening I led the dance in the Great Hall. Round the garden ran a very lofty wall, but I never cared to ask what lay beyond it, everything about me was so beautiful. My courtiers called me the Happy Prince, and happy indeed I was, if pleasure be happiness. So I lived, and so I died. And now that I am dead they have set me up here so high that I can see all the ugliness and all the misery of my city, and though my heart is made of lead yet I cannot choose but weep."

"What! Is he not of solid gold?" said the Swallow to himself. He was too polite to make any personal remarks out loud.

"Far away," continued the statue in a low musical voice, "far away in a little street there is a poor house. One of the

Sans-Souci: a French expression meaning "without worry, carefree"

windows is open, and through it I can see a woman seated at a table. Her face is thin and worn, and she has coarse, red hands, all pricked by the needle, for she is a seamstress. She is embroidering passion-flowers on a satin gown for the loveliest of the Queen's maids-of-honor to wear at the next court ball. In a bed in the corner of the room her little boy is lying ill. He has a fever, and is asking for oranges. His mother has nothing to give him but river water, so he is crying. Swallow, Swallow, little Swallow, will you not bring her the ruby out of my sword-hilt? My feet are fastened to this pedestal and I cannot move."

"I am waited for in Egypt," said the Swallow. "My friends are flying up and down the Nile, and talking to the large lotus flowers. Soon they will go to sleep in the tomb of the great king. The king is there himself in his painted coffin. He is wrapped in yellow linen, and embalmed with spices. Round his neck is a chain of pale green jade, and his hands are like withered leaves."

"Swallow, Swallow, little Swallow," said the Prince, "will you not stay with me for one night, and be my messenger? The boy is so thirsty, and the mother so sad."

"I don't think I like boys," answered the Swallow. "Last summer, when I was staying on the river, there were two rude boys, the miller's sons, who were always throwing stones at me. They never hit me, of course; we swallows fly far too well for that, and besides, I come of a family famous for its agility, but still, it was a mark of disrespect."

But the Happy Prince looked so sad that the little Swallow was sorry. "It is very cold here," he said, "but I will stay with you for one night, and be your messenger."

coarse: rough
agility: quickness, balance, and nimbleness

"Thank you, little Swallow," said the Prince.

So the Swallow picked out the great ruby from the Prince's sword, and flew away with it in his beak over the roofs of the town.

He passed by the cathedral tower, where the white marble angels were sculptured. He passed by the palace and heard the sound of dancing. A beautiful girl came out on the balcony with her beloved. "How wonderful the stars are," he said to her, "and how wonderful is the power of love!"

"I hope my dress will be ready in time for the ball," she answered. "I have ordered passion-flowers to be embroidered on it, but the seamstresses are so lazy."

He passed over the river, and saw the lanterns hanging to the masts of the ships. At last he came to the poor house and looked in. The boy was tossing feverishly on his bed, and the mother had fallen asleep, she was so tired. In he hopped, and laid the great ruby on the table beside the woman's thimble. Then he flew gently round the bed, fanning the boy's forehead with his wings. "How cool I feel," said the boy; "I must be getting better." And he sank into a delicious slumber.

Then the Swallow flew back to the Happy Prince, and told him what he had done. "It is curious," he remarked, "but I feel quite warm now, although it is so cold."

"That is because you have done a good deed," said the Prince. And the little Swallow began to think, and then he fell asleep. Thinking always made him sleepy.

When day broke he flew down to the river and had a bath. "Tonight I go to Egypt," said the Swallow, and he was in high spirits at the prospect. He visited all the public monuments, and sat a long time on top of the church steeple. Wherever he went the sparrows chirruped, and said to each other, "What a distinguished stranger!" so he enjoyed himself very much.

When the moon rose he flew back to the Happy Prince. "Have you any commissions for Egypt?" he cried; "I am just starting."

"Swallow, Swallow, little Swallow," said the Prince, "will you not stay with me one night longer? Far away across the city I see a young man in a garret. He is leaning over a desk covered with papers, and in a tumbler by his side there is a bunch of withered violets. His hair is brown and crisp, and his lips are red as a pomegranate, and he has large and dreamy eyes. He is trying to finish a play for the Director of the Theatre, but he is too cold to write any more. There is no fire in the grate, and hunger has made him faint."

"I will wait with you one night longer," said the Swallow, who really had a good heart. "Shall I take him another ruby?"

"Alas! I have no ruby now," said the Prince. "My eyes are all that I have left. They are made of rare sapphires, which were brought out of India a thousand years ago. Pluck out one of them and take it to him. He will sell it to the jeweler, and buy food and firewood, and finish his play."

"Dear Prince," said the Swallow, "I cannot do that," and he began to weep.

"Swallow, Swallow, little Swallow," said the Prince, "do as I command you."

---

garret: an attic apartment

tumbler: a drinking glass

pomegranate: a red fruit with many seeds

grate: fireplace; or, in a fireplace, a frame of bars for holding wood, coal, or other fuel

So the Swallow plucked out the Prince's eye, and flew away to the student's garret. It was easy enough to get in, as there was a hole in the roof. Through this he darted, and came into the room. The young man had his head buried in his hands, so he did not hear the flutter of the bird's wings, and when he looked up he found the beautiful sapphire lying on the withered violets.

"I am beginning to be appreciated," he cried; "this is from some great admirer. Now I can finish my play," and he looked quite happy.

The next day the Swallow flew down to the harbor. He sat on the mast of a large vessel and watched the sailors hauling big chests out of the hold with ropes. "I am going to Egypt!" cried the Swallow, but nobody minded, and when the moon rose he flew back to the Happy Prince.

"I am come to bid you good-bye," he cried.

"Swallow, Swallow, little Swallow," said the Prince, "will you not stay with me one night longer?"

"It is winter," answered the Swallow, "and the chill snow will soon be here. In Egypt the sun is warm on the green palm-trees, and the crocodiles lie in the mud and look lazily about them. Dear Prince, I must leave you, but I will never forget you, and next spring I will bring you back two beautiful jewels in place of those you have given away. The ruby shall be redder than a red rose, and the sapphire shall be as blue as the great sea."

"In the square below," said the Happy Prince, "there stands a little match girl. She has let her matches fall in the gutter, and they are all spoiled. Her father will beat her if she does not bring home some money, and she is crying. She has no shoes or stockings, and her little head is bare. Pluck out my other eye, and give it to her, and her father will not beat her."

"I will stay with you one night longer," said the Swallow, "but I cannot pluck out your eye. You would be quite blind then."

"Swallow, Swallow, little Swallow," said the Prince, "do as I command you."

So he plucked out the Prince's other eye, and darted down with it. He swooped past the match girl, and slipped the jewel into the palm of her hand. "What a lovely bit of glass," cried the little girl, and she ran home laughing.

Then the Swallow came back to the Prince. "You are blind now," he said, "so I will stay with you always."

"No, little Swallow," said the poor Prince, "you must go away to Egypt."

"I will stay with you always," said the Swallow, and he slept at the Prince's feet.

All the next day he sat on the Prince's shoulder, and told him stories of what he had seen in strange lands. He told him of the red ibises, who stand in long rows on the banks of the Nile, and catch gold-fish in their beaks; of the Sphinx, who is as old as the world itself, and lives in the desert, and knows everything; and of the merchants who walk slowly by the side of their camels, and carry amber beads in their hands.

"Dear little Swallow," said the Prince, "you tell me of marvelous things, but more marvelous than anything is the suffering of men and of women. There is no Mystery so great as Misery. Fly over my city, little Swallow, and tell me what you see there."

---

ibises: stork-like birds

So the Swallow flew over the great city, and saw the rich making merry in their beautiful houses, while the beggars were sitting at the gates. He flew into dark lanes, and saw the pale faces of starving children. Under the archway of a bridge two little boys were lying in one another's arms to try and keep themselves warm. "How hungry we are!" they said. "You must not lie here," shouted the Watchman, and they wandered out into the rain.

Then he flew back and told the Prince what he had seen.

"I am covered with fine gold," said the Prince, "you must take it off, leaf by leaf, and give it to my poor; the living always think that gold can make them happy."

Leaf after leaf of the fine gold the Swallow picked off, till the Happy Prince looked quite dull and gray. Leaf after leaf of the fine gold he brought to the poor, and the children's faces grew rosier, and they laughed and played games in the street. "We have bread now!" they cried.

Then the snow came, and after the snow came the frost. The streets looked as if they were made of silver, they were so bright and glistening. Long icicles like crystal daggers hung down from the eaves of the houses, everybody went about in furs, and the little boys wore scarlet caps and skated on the ice.

The poor little Swallow grew colder and colder, but he would not leave the Prince, for he loved him too well. He picked up crumbs outside the baker's door when the baker was not looking and tried to keep himself warm by flapping his wings.

But at last he knew that he was going to die. He had just enough strength to fly up to the Prince's shoulder once more.

---

eaves: the overhanging sections of roofs

"Good-bye, dear Prince!" he murmured. "Will you let me kiss your hand?"

"I am glad that you are going to Egypt at last, little Swallow," said the Prince. "You have stayed too long here; but you must kiss me on the lips, for I love you."

"It is not to Egypt that I am going," said the Swallow. "I am going to the House of Death. Death is the brother of Sleep, is he not?"

And he kissed the Happy Prince on the lips, and fell down dead at his feet.

At that moment a curious crack sounded inside the statue, as if something had broken. The fact is that the leaden heart had snapped right in two. It certainly was a dreadfully hard frost.

Early the next morning the Mayor was walking in the square below in company with the Town Councilors. As they passed the column he looked up at the statue. "Dear me! How shabby the Happy Prince looks!" he said.

"How shabby indeed!" cried the Town Councilors, who always agreed with the Mayor, and they went up to look at it.

"The ruby has fallen out of his sword, his eyes are gone, and he is golden no longer," said the Mayor. "In fact, he is little better than a beggar!"

"Little better than a beggar," said the Town Councilors.

"And here is actually a dead bird at his feet!" continued the Mayor. "We must really issue a proclamation that birds are not to be allowed to die here." And the Town Clerk made a note of the suggestion.

So they pulled down the statue of the Happy Prince. "As he is no longer beautiful, he is no longer useful," said the Art Professor at the University.

Then they melted the statue in a furnace, and the Mayor held a meeting of the Corporation to decide what was to be done with the metal. "We must have another statue, of course," he said, "and it shall be a statue of myself."

"Of myself," said each of the Town Councilors, and they quarreled. When I last heard of them they were quarrelling still.

"What a strange thing!" said the overseer of the workmen at the foundry. "This broken lead heart will not melt in the furnace. We must throw it away." So they threw it on a dust heap where the dead Swallow was also lying.

"Bring me the two most precious things in the city," said God to one of His Angels; and the Angel brought Him the leaden heart and the dead bird.

"You have rightly chosen," said God, "for in my garden of Paradise this little bird shall sing for evermore, and in my city of gold the Happy Prince shall praise me."

---

corporation: the city leaders
foundry: a business where metal is melted and shaped

# A PSALM OF LIFE

*by Henry Wadsworth Longfellow*

Tell me not, in mournful numbers,
"Life is but an empty dream!"
For the soul is dead that slumbers,
And things arc not what they seem.

Life is real! Life is earnest!
And the grave is not its goal;
"Dust thou art, to dust returnest,"
Was not spoken of the soul.

Not enjoyment, and not sorrow,
Is our destined end or way;
But to act, that each tomorrow
Find us farther than today.

Art is long, and Time is fleeting,
And our hearts, though stout and brave,
Still, like muffled drums, are beating
Funeral marches to the grave.

mournful: sad; full of sorrow
slumbers: sleeps
earnest: serious and sincere
fleeting: passing quickly
stout: sturdy or strong
muffled: quieted

In the world's broad field of battle,
In the bivouac of Life,
Be not like dumb, driven cattle!
Be a hero in the strife!

Trust no Future, howe'er pleasant!
Let the dead Past bury its dead!
Act—act in the living Present!
Heart within, and God o'erhead!

Lives of great men all remind us
We can make our lives sublime,
And, departing, leave behind us
Footprints on the sands of time;

Footprints, that perhaps another,
Sailing o'er life's solemn main,
A forlorn and shipwrecked brother,
Seeing, shall take heart again.

Let us, then, be up and doing,
With a heart for any fate;
Still achieving, still pursuing,
Learn to labor and to wait.

---

bivouac: a camp for soldiers
strife: fighting, conflict
sublime: grand; inspiring awe and wonder
solemn: deeply serious
forlorn: deserted; sad and lonely

# STORIES FROM THE BIBLE

# BELSHAZZAR'S FEAST:
# THE HANDWRITING ON THE WALL

In days long past, King Nebuchadnezzar attacked the city of Jerusalem, raided the treasures of the Temple, and marched thousands of sons and daughters of Israel back with him to Babylon.

In time, the crown of Babylon passed to his son, Belshazzar. All was well for the new king, until one night he held a great feast for a thousand of his lords.

That night, from the kitchens came a never-ending parade of delicious dishes, and fine wine flowed like water. Belshazzar ate and drank until he was dizzy. Then he gulped the last of the wine in his goblet, rose to his feet, and said, "Bring in the gold and silver vessels my father took from the Temple in Jerusalem. What more fitting cups are there for us to drink from?"

The king's servants brought in the sacred vessels of the Temple, and filled them with the wine of Babylon. And Belshazzar and his lords drank deep, praising their gods of gold and silver, of brass and iron, of wood and stone.

Not an hour had passed when, suddenly, a hand appeared in mid-air, and began to write upon the palace wall. Belshazzar's flushed face grew pale and his knees knocked together as he watched the letters appear in the plaster. Four words the hand wrote; and then it vanished.

---

vessels: containers for liquids

A thousand imaginings, each more terrible than the last, raced through Belshazzar's head, for he could not read what the hand had written. "Fetch the astrologers!" he cried. "Summon the Chaldeans. Call the soothsayers—at once!"

When the wise men of Babylon arrived, he said to them, "Whoever can read this writing and tell me what it means will be clothed in scarlet and have a chain of gold about his neck, and I will make him the third ruler of the kingdom."

The wise men looked at the writing, but none of them could read it or tell what it meant. Belshazzar was greatly troubled. His face grew gray and sickly, and all his lords were astonished at the change in him.

Then the door opened, and the queen entered the banquet hall, for she had heard of the strange hand, the figures it had wrought, and the king's distress. She went to Belshazzar and said, "O king, live forever! Do not let your thoughts trouble you, do not let yourself be moved! There is in your kingdom a man named Daniel who is so wise that your father made him the master of all the wise men in Babylon. In the days of your father, light and understanding and wisdom were found in him. Let Daniel be called, and he will read you the words and tell you their meaning."

So Daniel was called and brought before the king.

"Are you the Daniel who is one of the sons of the captivity of Judah, whom the king my father brought out of Jerusalem?" said Belshazzar. "I have heard of you. I have

astrologers: people who study the stars and planets to determine their
    effect on people's lives
soothsayers: persons who, it was believed, could predict the future
wrought: created

heard that light, understanding, and excellent wisdom are found in you.

"All the wise men in Babylon could not tell me the meaning of the writing on that wall," he continued, "but I have heard that you can find the hidden meanings of things and explain enigmas. Now, if you can read this writing and tell me what it means, you will be clothed with scarlet and have a chain of gold around your neck, and I will make you the third ruler in the kingdom."

"Give your gifts to yourself and your rewards to another," said Daniel, "for I do not want them. But I will read to you the writing and tell you what it means."

Then Daniel said, "O king, the most high God gave Nebuchadnezzar your father a kingdom and majesty, glory, and honor. And because of the majesty that he gave him, all people, nations, and languages trembled and feared before him. Whomever he wished, he set up; and whomever he wished, he put down.

"But when his heart was lifted up, and his spirit hardened in pride, he was deposed from his kingly throne, and they took his glory from him. Then he was driven from the sons of men, and his heart was made like the beasts, and his dwelling was with the animals. They fed him with grass like oxen, and his body was wet with the dew of heaven, till he knew that the most high God ruled in the kingdom of men, and that he appoints over it whomever he chooses.

"But you, his son, Belshazzar, have not humbled your heart, though you know all this. You have lifted yourself up against the Lord of heaven. They brought the vessels of his house before you, and you and your lords drank wine from

---

enigmas: mysterious words; things very hard to understand or explain
deposed: removed from power

them. And you praised the gods of gold and silver, bronze and iron, wood and stone, which do not see or hear or know; and the God who holds your breath in his hand and owns all your ways, you have not glorified.

"So that is why he has sent the hand which has written these words: *Mene, Mene, Tekel, Parsin*. And the meaning of the words is this:

> *Mene:* God has numbered your kingdom, and finished it.
> *Tekel:* You have been weighed in the balances and are found wanting.
> *Parsin:* Your kingdom is divided, and given to the Medes and the Persians."

And that very night, the Persians conquered the city and slew Belshazzar, the king of Babylon.

---

wanting: below expectations
slew: killed

# How Queen Esther Saved Her People

Long ago, a king named Ahasuerus ruled over the vast empire of Persia. This king decided to hold a great feast, to which he invited all the princes and nobles of his kingdom. In the beautiful gardens of the palace, where hangings of white and green and blue were fastened with silver rings to pillars of marble, the men drank wine from goblets of gold.

On the seventh day of the feast, when the heart of the king was merry with wine, he was struck by a fancy to show off his beautiful queen, Vashti, to his guests. The king commanded his servants to bring the queen to the feast. But Vashti refused to be paraded before these men.

When the king heard this, his fury flared. Some of his guests, who had little respect for women, advised him to punish Vashti. After all, they said, if wives throughout the kingdom began to hear how the queen had disobeyed the king, then they might begin to disobey their husbands.

And so, in his wrath, Ahasuerus ordered that Vashti be banished from the kingdom.

Now came the task of finding a new queen for the king. Servants were sent far and wide to find the most beautiful maidens in the kingdom. Among those who were brought to the palace was a girl who was as good as she was lovely, by the name of Esther.

---

fancy: a whim; a sudden, impulsive idea
banished: sent away permanently; exiled

In the king's eyes, Esther, with her simple beauty and royal bearing, far exceeded in grace and favor all the other maidens, though they were dressed in the richest finery and doused with costly perfumes. So he set the royal crown upon Esther's head and made her queen instead of Vashti. And, taking his new queen's hand, the king proclaimed their wedding day a holiday in all the provinces.

There was one thing the king did not know—that Esther came from a Jewish family. She had been raised by an older cousin, named Mordecai. Mordecai had cared for her as though she were his own daughter, and Esther loved and trusted him completely. And so she followed Mordecai's guidance when he told her, "There is one thing you must not do: tell neither the king nor anyone else that you come from among the Jews."

Mordecai came each day to the palace to talk with Esther. But one day, he hurried into the courtyard and said to her, "While I was sitting by the palace gate, I heard two servants plotting to kill the king. Now fly to Ahasuerus and tell him the news."

"I cannot," whispered Esther. "The king has an iron rule: no one, not even I, the queen, may come before him who has not been summoned. If I disobey, the price is death."

"If you obey, the price is also death—the king's," said Mordecai. "Go!"

Bravely, Esther went to the king's inner court and stood upon the threshold. If the king were in one of his wild tempers, it might mean her death. When the king saw her, he

---

doused: covered with a liquid
threshold: doorsill; the point of entrance to a room

raised his eyebrows, but then he lifted his golden scepter, which was the sign that her life was spared.

Esther gave him Mordecai's message, and the king at once sent his ministers to find out if Mordecai's words were true. A short time later, the ministers returned with the guilty servants, who were soon put to death as traitors. When all was done, an account of this action, along with Mordecai's role in it, was written in the book of chronicles, a history of the happenings in the king's court.

At this same time, a proud and jealous man named Haman was becoming the new favorite of King Ahasuerus. As Haman rose in power, he commanded all to do him homage. So all the people bowed to Haman in fear and trembling as he passed—all but Mordecai, who stood straight and proud.

"Why don't you bow?" Haman's servants demanded.

Mordecai replied, "I humble myself before no man, only before God."

When Haman heard this, he raged, "I will punish this upstart. I will break his stiff neck. If he will not bow before me—he and all his people—I will trample them into the mud."

Then Haman went to King Ahasuerus and said, "O king, live forever! The Jews live in every province of the kingdom, but their laws are different from other people's, and they disobey the king's commands. Do not let them remain. Instead, let a decree be written that they be destroyed."

---

scepter: a staff or baton used as symbol of authority
homage: expression of great respect or public honor
upstart: a person who acts more important than he or she really is
decree: an official order

Ahasuerus trusted Haman, and he was so quick to anger that he did not even stop to ask for an explanation. Instead, he took from his finger a signet ring with the royal seal upon it, and, giving this to Haman, he said, "The people are given to you. Do with them what seems good to you."

A short while later, a decree went out from the palace that said that all the Jews—young and old, men, women, and children—were to be killed on a single day, and their possessions plundered for the king's treasury. And as it was sealed with the king's seal, it was made law.

That day, a servant came to Queen Esther and told her that Mordecai stood waiting for her at the gates, dressed all in sackcloth and covered with ashes.

Esther rushed out to see him. "What is wrong?" she cried. "Why are you in mourning?"

Mordecai told her of the terrible edict. "You must go to the king again," he said, "and plead for the lives of your people."

"I cannot," replied Esther. "I have not been called in to see the king for many days. If I go to him again without being summoned, he will certainly have me killed."

"Do not think in your heart that you will escape death in the king's palace any more than all the other Jews," said Mordecai. "For if you remain silent now, you and your father's house will perish. But who knows that you did not come to the kingdom for this very reason?"

"Go," said Esther. "Tell all the Jews to eat and drink nothing for three days and nights and to pray for

---

signet: an official seal, usually used to mark a document
sackcloth: a rough cloth worn as sign of mourning
edict: a decree; a command made by a ruler

deliverance from this cruel fate. Then I will go before the king. And if I perish, I perish."

Four days later, Esther put on her royal robes and made her way along the silent marble hall to the king's inner court.

When Ahasuerus looked up and saw her, trembling but resolute, he was captivated by her beauty and courage. He raised his golden scepter, and she knew that once again her life had been spared.

"What does my queen desire?" asked the king. "Even though it be half my kingdom, it will be yours!"

Then Esther said, "If it pleases the king, do me the honor to attend with Haman a feast that I have prepared for your pleasure."

The King was very pleased. "Indeed, it shall be as you wish," he replied. Then he turned to his servants and said, "Bring Haman quickly, that he may do what Esther has said."

The king and Haman went to Queen Esther's banquet. There, Ahasuerus said to Esther, "Tell me, what do you wish? Whatever it is, I will give it to you, even though it be half my kingdom."

"O king," replied Esther, "if I have found favor in your eyes, come to the banquet I will prepare for you tomorrow, and bring Haman with you. I will ask you for something then."

That day, Haman left the palace joyful and with a glad heart. But when he passed Mordecai at the gate, and the man did not bow or tremble before him, it was as though a dark cloud passed over his face. When he reached home, he called his friends and his wife to him and said, "I have great riches and many children, and the highest place in the kingdom next to the king himself. Even the queen invited no one but

deliverance: an act of rescue

me to come with the king to the banquet she prepared, and tomorrow I am invited to dine with him again. But what is any of this worth when that man Mordecai defies me at the king's gate?"

His friends suggested to him, "Have a gallows made, fifty cubits high. In the morning, suggest to the king that Mordecai be hanged on it. Then go merrily with the king to the banquet."

The idea pleased Haman, and he planned to have the gallows built the next day.

Back in the palace, though, the King found that he could not sleep. So he called to his chamberlain and asked him to read from the book of chronicles to soothe him. As Ahasuerus listened, he heard the story of the two men who had plotted to kill him, and how Mordecai had overheard the traitors and sent warning.

"Has this man been rewarded?" asked Ahasuerus.

"No, sire," replied the servant.

So the king sent for Haman and asked, "How should a king honor a man whom he wishes to reward?"

Haman thought, "The king wishes to honor me!" So he replied, "Clothe this man in the king's finest robes, mount him on the king's charger, and have a great noble lead him through the city streets, crying, 'Thus shall be done to a man whom the king delights to honor.'"

"An excellent idea, Haman!" said the king. "Now, find Mordecai. Clothe him in my finest robes, lead him through the city streets on my finest stallion, and honor him as you have directed, for he has saved my life."

gallows: structure used for hanging condemned criminals
cubits: an ancient unit of length, from the middle finger to the elbow
chamberlain: an official in charge of the king's household

Haman was stunned, but he could do nothing but carry out the royal command.

That evening, the king and Haman went to Esther's banquet. When the king had eaten and drunk his fill, he turned to Esther and said, "Now, my dear queen, what can I do for you?"

"If I have really won your favor, O king," replied Esther, "grant me my life and the lives of my people. For I am Jewish, and you have decreed that my people are to be slain!"

"What?" roared the king, his wineglass crashing to the marble floor. "Who has arranged this treachery? Who dares harm my queen?"

"Your enemy is here!" cried Esther. "It is the wicked Haman."

As the king stormed into the courtyard to call the guards, Haman threw himself at Esther's feet. "Mercy, O queen," he cried, "mercy!"

At that moment, Ahasuerus returned, and when he saw Haman clutching at Esther, he cried, "Will you attack the queen while I am even in the house?"

As the guards dragged Haman away, one pointed into the distance and said, "Behold the gallows that Haman has made for Mordecai!"

"Take Haman and hang him on it," said the king grimly. And so Haman met the very fate he had intended for Mordecai.

That is the story of Esther. Since that time, on the holiday known as Purim, the Jewish people have been glad to remember the queen whose courage and wisdom helped to save her people.

---

treachery: deception; betrayal

# The Story of Jonah

**O**nce there lived a man named Jonah, who was full of righteousness. One day, God called to Jonah and said, "Arise, and go to the great city of Nineveh. Cry out to the people against their wickedness, for they have grown evil. They must mend their ways, or I will destroy them."

"Why me, Lord?" cried Jonah. "Nineveh is far from here, and the Ninevites are my enemies and the enemies of my people. And they worship other gods, so they will not listen to me. Why should I go to so much trouble to save them? If they are evil, why should I care if they are destroyed? Besides, you are a gracious and merciful God. I am sure you will forgive them anyway."

But the Lord did not answer him.

So Jonah decided to run away. He went down to the sea and found a ship sailing in the opposite direction from Nineveh, toward Tarshish. He paid the fare, and hid himself deep in the ship's hold. "God will not find me here," he thought, and he fell fast asleep.

The sun was shining and the sea was calm as the ship sailed out of the harbor. But when the city disappeared over the horizon, the sky went black, and a great wind came rushing over the water, churning up waves that towered over the little boat before crashing down upon the decks.

---

mend: to improve; to reform; to make free of faults
churning: making a violent motion

The ship's planks splintered and began to crack. Terror seized every man aboard, and each prayed to his own gods to end the storm. But the waves only battered them more fiercely, and the boat began to sink.

As the men frantically threw the ship's cargo into the sea, trying to lighten the load to help the craft stay afloat, the captain remembered Jonah. He found him in the hold, still asleep. "How can you sleep?" he cried. "Arise, and call upon your God. Perhaps he will save us, for we are about to die."

Jonah followed the captain to the deck, where all the sailors were laboring to keep the little craft afloat. But the storm grew worse, and they feared the ship would soon be broken to pieces. "Come," they said, "let us cast lots. Then we will know who has brought the storm upon us," for that was the custom of their time.

So they cast the lots, and the lot fell on Jonah.

"Who are you?" cried the sailors to Jonah, "and what have you done that you bring such trouble with you?"

Jonah replied, "I am a Hebrew, and I disobeyed my God. I thought I could flee from him by sailing over the sea. But he made the sea as well as the land, and I am found."

"What should we do to calm the sea?" asked the sailors.

"Pick me up and throw me into the sea," said Jonah. "Then the storm will end, for it has only come for my sake."

But not a single man would lift his hand against Jonah. Instead, they again took up their oars and rowed with all their strength toward land. Yet the harder they rowed, the more the waves drove them back.

frantically: with wild, uncontrolled, desperate excitement
cast lots: to make a choice, similar to drawing straws

At last, they put down their oars and cried, "Lord, do not punish us if this man loses his life. We are only doing what he charges us to do in your name."

So they took up Jonah and cast him into the sea, and the sea ceased from its raging. The water grew calm and as smooth as glass, and the wonder-struck men rowed safely on.

As for Jonah, he was swept beneath the waves, but not to his death. For the Lord had prepared a great fish to swallow Jonah. For three days and nights he sat alone in the dark belly of the great fish. Then Jonah prayed:

"I cried out to the Lord because of my affliction, and you heard my voice. You had cast me into the deep, in the midst of the seas, and the floods compassed me about, and the waves passed over me.

"The waters surrounded me even to my soul, the deep closed around me, and weeds were wrapped around my head.

"I went down to the bottoms of the mountains, yet you have brought up my life from the pit, O Lord.

"When my soul fainted within me, I remembered the Lord, and my prayer went up to you."

Then the Lord spoke to the fish, and it vomited Jonah onto dry land.

"Arise," said God to Jonah. "Go to the great city of Nineveh, and preach to it the message that I tell you."

So Jonah arose, and did as the Lord had spoken.

Nineveh was an enormous city, the capital of an empire, and a three-day journey from gate to gate. As soon as Jonah entered, and for many days after, with every step he cried,

---

affliction: suffering
compassed: encircled

"Oh Nineveh! Your wickedness has come up before the Lord! Repent, or in forty days, you and your city will be overthrown!"

And the people of Nineveh listened to him and believed. The king arose from his throne and laid aside his robe, covered himself with sackcloth, and sat in a pile of ashes. Then he sent out a decree that said: "Let neither man nor beast, herd nor flock, taste anything; do not let them eat or drink water. But let man and beast be covered with sackcloth and cry mightily to God. Let every one turn from his evil way and from the violence that is in his hands. Who can tell if God will turn away from his fierce anger, so that we may not perish?"

So all, from the greatest to the least of them, mourned and prayed over their wickedness, and fasted and covered themselves, and even their animals, in sackcloth. And God saw their works and knew they turned from their evil ways. So at the end of the forty days, God did not bring disaster on the city.

But Jonah was furious. "Ah, Lord," he cried, "was this not what I said while I was still in my country? This is why I tried to flee to Tarshish. I know that you are a gracious and merciful God, slow to anger, and overflowing with loving kindness. I knew you would do them no harm. Why then did I have to come here? It would be better now for me to die than to live."

God replied, "Is it right for you to be angry?"

But Jonah did not answer him. Instead, he left Nineveh and climbed a high hill, so he could sit and watch what

repent: to turn away from sin; to change as a result of regret for
  one's bad actions
sackcloth: a rough cloth worn as sign of mourning

would become of the city. The sun beat down on his head, but Jonah would not be moved. He only sat there and watched.

One night, God made a tree grow up over Jonah, to bring him shade and cheer. Jonah was glad and grateful for the tree. But as morning dawned the next day, God sent a worm that did so much damage, the tree withered and died.

As the sun again beat down on Jonah, Jonah almost fainted. "Here am I," he thought, "with this poor tree, both suffering unto death, while the wicked people of Nineveh are forgiven and full of joy." Then he cried out, "Oh Lord, it would be better for me to die than to live."

The Lord said, "Is it right for you to be angry about the tree?"

Jonah replied, "Yes, it is right for me to be angry. In fact, I will be angry until I die!"

"Jonah," said God, "you feel pity for a tree that you did not make or take care of, that came up in a night and perished in a night. Should I not pity Nineveh, that great city, where there are more than one hundred and twenty thousand people who do not know the difference between their right hand and their left—and many cattle besides?"

# STORIES IN VERSE

## NARRATIVE POEMS

# CASABIANCA

*by Felicia Hemans*

The boy stood on the burning deck
    Whence all but he had fled;
The flame that lit the battle's wreck
    Shone round him o'er the dead.

The flames rolled on. He would not go
    Without his father's word;
That father faint in death below,
    His voice no longer heard.

He called aloud: "Say, father, say
    If yet my task is done!"
He knew not that the chieftain lay
    Unconscious of his son.

"Speak, father!" once again he cried,
    "If I may yet be gone!"
And but the booming shots replied,
    And fast the flames rolled on.

Upon his brow he felt their breath,
    And in his waving hair,
And looked from that lone post of death
    In still yet brave despair;

---

whence: from which place
faint: weak; unaware
chieftain: a leader
unconscious: unaware
still: calm; quiet

And shouted but once more aloud,
    "My father! must I stay?"
While o'er him fast through sail and shroud,
    The wreathing fires made way.

They wrapt the ship in splendor wild,
    They caught the flag on high,
And streamed above the gallant child
    Like banners in the sky.

Then came a burst of thunder-sound—
    The boy—oh! where was he?
Ask of the winds that far around
    With fragments strewed the sea,

With mast, and helm and pennon fair,
    That well had borne their part.
But the noblest thing which perished there
    Was that young faithful heart.

shroud: a supporting rope on a ship
wreathing: encircling; curling or twisting
wrapt: wrapped; covered
splendor: brilliant light; magnificence
gallant: brave; courageous
strewed: scattered or covered
pennon: a banner carried on a spear or lance
perished: died

# THE INCHCAPE ROCK
### *by Robert Southey*

No stir in the air, no stir in the sea,
The ship was as still as she could be;
Her sails from heaven received no motion;
Her keel was steady in the ocean.

Without either sign or sound of their shock
The waves flowed over the Inchcape Rock;
So little they rose, so little they fell,
They did not move the Inchcape Bell.

The good old Abbot of Aberbrothok
Had placed that bell on the Inchcape Rock;
On a buoy in the storm it floated and swung,
And over the waves its warning rung.

When the rock was hid by the surges' swell,
The mariners heard the warning bell;
And then they knew the perilous rock
And blessed the Abbot of Aberbrothok.

---

stir: movement
keel: the center beam running under a ship
abbot: a leader of a monastery
buoy: a floating object in water used to mark a route or
    indicate danger
surges: waves
mariners: sailors
perilous: dangerous

The sun in heaven was shining gay,—
All things were joyful on that day;
The sea birds screamed as they wheeled around,
And there was joyance in their sound.

The buoy of the Inchcape Bell was seen,
A darker spot on the ocean green;
Sir Ralph the Rover walked his deck
And he fixed his eye on the darker speck.

He felt the cheering power of spring,—
It made him whistle, it made him sing;
His heart was mirthful to excess,
But the Rover's mirth was wickedness.

His eye was on the Inchcape float.
Quoth he, "My men, put out the boat
And row me to the Inchcape Rock,
And I'll plague the Abbot of Aberbrothok."

The boat is lowered, the boatmen row,
And to the Inchcape Rock they go;
Sir Ralph bent over from the boat,
And he cut the bell from the Inchcape float.

Down sank the bell with a gurgling sound;
The bubbles rose and burst around.
Quoth Sir Ralph, "The next who comes to the Rock
Won't bless the Abbot of Aberbrothok."

---

joyance: delight; joy
mirthful: happy; gleeful
plague: to annoy or bother

Sir Ralph the Rover sail'd away,—
He scoured the seas for many a day;
And now, grown rich with plundered store,
He steers his course for Scotland's shore.

So thick a haze o'erspreads the sky
They cannot see the sun on high;
The wind hath blown a gale all day;
At evening it hath died away.

On the deck the Rover takes his stand;
So dark it is they see no land.
Quoth Sir Ralph, "It will be lighter soon,
For there is the dawn of the rising moon."

"Canst hear," said one, "the breakers roar?
Methinks we should be near the shore."
"Now where we are I cannot tell,
But I wish I could hear the Inchcape Bell."

They hear no sound; the swell is strong;
Though the wind hath fallen, they drift along
Till the vessel strikes with a shivering shock,
Full on the ledge of the Inchcape Rock!

Sir Ralph the Rover tore his hair;
He curst himself in his despair;
The waves rush in on every side—
The ship is sinking beneath the tide.

scoured: searched
plundered: stolen; taken by force
curst: cursed

# THE LISTENERS
*by Walter de la Mare*

"Is there anybody there?" said the Traveler,
    Knocking on the moonlit door;
And his horse in the silence champed the grasses
    Of the forest's ferny floor:
And a bird flew up out of the turret,
    Above the Traveler's head:
And he smote upon the door again a second time;
    "Is there anybody there?" he said.
But no one descended to the Traveler;
    No head from the leaf-fringed sill
Leaned over and looked into his gray eyes,
    Where he stood perplexed and still.
But only a host of phantom listeners
    That dwelt in the lone house then
Stood listening in the quiet of the moonlight
    To that voice from the world of men:
Stood thronging the faint moonbeams on the dark stair,
    That goes down to the empty hall,

champed: bit
turret: a castle's tower
smote: struck or hit
sill: the edge of a window
perplexed: puzzled; confused
host: a great many
phantom: ghostly
thronging: crowding

Hearkening in an air stirred and shaken
    By the lonely Traveler's call.
And he felt in his heart their strangeness,
    Their stillness answering his cry,
While his horse moved, cropping the dark turf,
    'Neath the starred and leafy sky;
For he suddenly smote on the door, even
    Louder, and lifted his head:—
"Tell them I came, and no one answered,
    That I kept my word," he said.
Never the least stir made the listeners,
    Though every word he spake
Fell echoing through the shadowiness of the still house
    From the one man left awake:
Ay, they heard his foot upon the stirrup,
    And the sound of iron on stone,
And how the silence surged softly backward,
    When the plunging hoofs were gone.

---

hearkening: listening
cropping: biting off the top parts
turf: the grass and ground beneath
'neath: poetic shortened form of "beneath"
spake: spoke

# CASEY AT THE BAT

*by Ernest Lawrence Thayer*

The outlook wasn't brilliant for the Mudville nine that day;
The score stood four to two with but one inning more to play.
And then when Cooney died at first, and Barrows did the same,
A sickly silence fell upon the patrons of the game.

A straggling few got up to go in deep despair. The rest
Clung to that hope which springs eternal in the human breast;
They thought if only Casey could but get a whack at that—
We'd put up even money now with Casey at the bat.

But Flynn preceded Casey, as did also Jimmy Blake,
And the former was a lulu and the latter was a cake;
So upon that stricken multitude grim melancholy sat,
For there seemed but little chance of Casey's getting to the bat.

But Flynn let drive a single, to the wonderment of all,
And Blake, the much despisèd, tore the cover off the ball;
And when the dust had lifted, and the men saw what had occurred,
There was Jimmy safe at second and Flynn a-hugging third.

patrons: supporters; customers; fans
straggling: wandering from the main way
preceded: came before
stricken: overwhelmed by sorrow, trouble, or misfortune
multitude: a crowd of people
melancholy: sadness; gloom
despisèd: hated

Then from five thousand throats and more there rose a lusty yell;
It rumbled through the valley, it rattled in the dell;
It knocked upon the mountain and recoiled upon the flat,
For Casey, mighty Casey, was advancing to the bat.

There was ease in Casey's manner as he stepped into his place;
There was pride in Casey's bearing and a smile on Casey's face.
And when, responding to the cheers, he lightly doffed his hat,
No stranger in the crowd could doubt 'twas Casey at the bat.

Ten thousand eyes were on him as he rubbed his hands with dirt;
Five thousand tongues applauded when he wiped them on his shirt.
Then while the writhing pitcher ground the ball into his hip,
Defiance gleamed in Casey's eye, a sneer curled Casey's lip.

And now the leather-covered sphere came hurtling through the air,
And Casey stood a-watching it in haughty grandeur there.
Close by the sturdy batsman the ball unheeded sped—
"That ain't my style," said Casey. "Strike one," the umpire said.

From the benches, black with people, there went up a muffled roar,
Like the beating of the storm waves on a stern and distant shore.
"Kill him! Kill the umpire!" shouted someone on the stand,
And it's likely they'd have killed him had not Casey raised his hand.

---

lusty: energetic; enthusiastic
recoiled: bounced back
doffed: took off for a moment; tipped
writhing: twisting
defiance: bold resistance
haughty: scornfully proud
grandeur: greatness; magnificence
unheeded: ignored

With a smile of Christian charity great Casey's visage shone;
He stilled the rising tumult; he bade the game go on;
He signaled to the pitcher, and once more the spheroid flew;
But Casey still ignored it, and the umpire said, "Strike two."

"Fraud!" cried the maddened thousands, and echo answered, "Fraud!"
But one scornful look from Casey and the audience was awed.
They saw his face grow stern and cold, they saw his muscles strain,
And they knew that Casey wouldn't let that ball go by again.

The sneer is gone from Casey's lip, his teeth are clenched in hate;
He pounds with cruel violence his bat upon the plate.
And now the pitcher holds the ball, and now he lets it go,
And now the air is shattered by the force of Casey's blow.

Oh, somewhere in this favored land the sun is shining bright;
The band is playing somewhere, and somewhere hearts are light,
And somewhere men are laughing, and somewhere children shout;
*But there is no joy in Mudville—mighty Casey has struck out.*

---

visage: face
tumult: confusion; commotion; uproar
spheroid: something in the shape of a sphere (in this case, the baseball)
fraud: fake; impostor; cheater

# THE CREMATION OF SAM MCGEE

### by Robert Service

*There are strange things done in the midnight sun*
  *By the men who moil for gold;*
*The Arctic trails have their secret tales*
  *That would make your blood run cold;*
*The Northern Lights have seen queer sights,*
  *But the queerest they ever did see*
*Was that night on the marge of Lake Lebarge*
  *I cremated Sam McGee.*

Now Sam McGee was from Tennessee,
  where the cotton blooms and blows.
Why he left his home in the South to roam
  'round the Pole, God only knows.
He was always cold, but the land of gold
  seemed to hold him like a spell;
Though he'd often say in his homely way
  that he'd "sooner live in hell."

On a Christmas Day we were mushing our way
  over the Dawson trail.
Talk of your cold! through the parka's fold
  it stabbed like a driven nail.

---

moil: to toil or work hard
marge: margin; edge
cremated: burned a dead body
homely: plain; simple
mushing: driving dogs over snow
parka: a warm coat with a hood

If our eyes we'd close, then the lashes froze
    till sometimes we couldn't see,
It wasn't much fun, but the only one
    to whimper was Sam McGee.

And that very night, as we lay packed tight
    in our robes beneath the snow,
And the dogs were fed, and the stars o'erhead
    were dancing heel and toe,
He turned to me, and "Cap," says he,
    "I'll cash in this trip, I guess;
And if I do, I'm asking that you
    won't refuse my last request."

Well, he seemed so low that I couldn't say no;
    then he says with a sort of moan,
"It's the cursed cold, and it's got right hold
    till I'm chilled clean through to the bone.
Yet 'tain't being dead—it's my awful dread
    of the icy grave that pains;
So I want you to swear that, foul or fair,
    you'll cremate my last remains."

A pal's last need is a thing to heed,
    so I swore I would not fail;
And we started on at the streak of dawn;
    but God! he looked ghastly pale.
He crouched on the sleigh, and he raved all day
    of his home in Tennessee;
And before nightfall a corpse was all
    that was left of Sam McGee.

---

ghastly: horribly; terrifyingly
corpse: a dead body

There wasn't a breath in that land of death,
    and I hurried, horror-driven,
With a corpse half hid that I couldn't get rid,
    because of a promise given;
It was lashed to the sleigh, and it seemed to say:
    "You may tax your brawn and brains,
But you promised true, and it's up to you
    to cremate these last remains."

Now a promise made is a debt unpaid,
    and the trail has its own stern code.
In the days to come, though my lips were dumb,
    in my heart how I cursed that load!
In the long, long night, by the lone firelight,
    while the huskies, round in a ring,
Howled out their woes to the homeless snows—
    O God, how I loathed the thing!

And every day that quiet clay
    seemed to heavy and heavier grow;
And on I went, though the dogs were spent
    and the grub was getting low.
The trail was bad, and I felt half mad,
    but I swore I would not give in;
And I'd often sing to the hateful thing,
    and it hearkened with a grin.

lashed: tied tightly
tax: to make hard demands on
dumb: unable to speak; silent
loathed: hated
spent: exhausted; worn out
grub: food
hearkened: listened

Till I came to the marge of Lake Lebarge,
    and a derelict there lay;
It was jammed in the ice, but I saw in a trice
    it was called the *Alice May*.
And I looked at it, and I thought a bit,
    and I looked at my frozen chum;
Then "Here," said I, with a sudden cry,
    "is my cre-ma-tor-eum."

Some planks I tore from the cabin floor,
    and I lit the boiler fire;
Some coal I found that was lying around,
    and I heaped the fuel higher;
The flames just soared, and the furnace roared—
    such a blaze you seldom see,
And I burrowed a hole in the glowing coal,
    and I stuffed in Sam McGee.

Then I made a hike, for I didn't like
    to hear him sizzle so;
And the heavens scowled, and the huskies howled,
    and the wind began to blow.
It was icy cold, but the hot sweat rolled
    down my cheeks, and I don't know why;
And the greasy smoke in an inky cloak
    went streaking down the sky.

---

derelict: something abandoned (in this case, a deserted ship)
in a trice: an expression meaning "in an instant"

I do not know how long in the snow
    I wrestled with grisly fear;
But the stars came out and they danced about
    ere again I ventured near;
I was sick with dread, but I bravely said,
    "I'll just take a peep inside.
I guess he's cooked, and it's time I looked."
    Then the door I opened wide.

And there sat Sam, looking cool and calm,
    in the heart of the furnace roar;
And he wore a smile you could see a mile,
    and he said, "Please close that door.
It's fine in here, but I greatly fear
    you'll let in the cold and storm—
Since I left Plumtree, down in Tennessee,
    it's the first time I've been warm."

*There are strange things done in the midnight sun*
    *By the men who moil for gold;*
*The Arctic trails have their secret tales*
    *That would make your blood run cold;*
*The Northern Lights have seen queer sights,*
    *But the queerest they ever did see*
*Was that night on the marge of Lake Lebarge*
    *I cremated Sam McGee.*

---

grisly: terrifying
ere: an old-fashioned word for "before"
ventured: proceeded in something risky

# THE HIGHWAYMAN
*by Alfred Noyes*

### PART I

The wind was a torrent of darkness among the gusty trees,
The moon was a ghostly galleon tossed upon cloudy seas,
The road was a ribbon of moonlight over the purple moor,
And the highwayman came riding—
    Riding—riding—
The highwayman came riding, up to the old inn-door.

He'd a French cocked-hat on his forehead, a bunch of lace
    at his chin,
A coat of the claret velvet, and breeches of brown doe-skin;
They fitted with never a wrinkle; his boots were up to the thigh!
And he rode with a jeweled twinkle,
    His pistol butts a-twinkle,
His rapier hilt a-twinkle, under the jeweled sky.

Over the cobbles he clattered and clashed in the dark inn-yard,
And he tapped with his whip on the shutters, but all was locked
    and barred:
He whistled a tune to the window, and who should be waiting there

---

torrent: a violent flood
galleon: a large sailing ship
moor: an open field or plain
claret: dark purplish red (like the color of the wine called claret)
breeches: knee-length pants
rapier: a long sword
hilt: a handle, especially of a sword
cobbles: cobblestones; round stones used in old roads

But the landlord's black-eyed daughter,
    Bess, the landlord's daughter,
Plaiting a dark red love-knot into her long black hair.

And dark in the dark old inn-yard a stable-wicket creaked
Where Tim the ostler listened; his face was white and peaked;
His eyes were hollows of madness, his hair like moldy hay,
But he loved the landlord's daughter,
    The landlord's red-lipped daughter,
Dumb as a dog he listened, and he heard the robber say—

"One kiss, my bonny sweetheart, I'm after a prize to-night,
But I shall be back with the yellow gold before the morning light;
Yet, if they press me sharply, and harry me through the day,
Then look for me by moonlight,
    Watch for me by moonlight,
I'll come to thee by moonlight, though hell should bar the way."

He rose upright in the stirrups; he scarce could reach her hand,
But she loosened her hair i' the casement! His face burned like
        a brand
As the black cascade of perfume came tumbling over his breast;
And he kissed its waves in the moonlight,
    (Oh, sweet black waves in the moonlight!)
Then he tugged at his rein in the moonlight, and galloped away
        to the West.

---

plaiting: braiding
stable-wicket: a gate to the stable
ostler: someone who takes care of horses
peaked: pale
harry: to force to move along; to disturb constantly
casement: a window frame
brand: torch; a piece of burning wood
cascade: a waterfall, thus, anything that falls or rushes forth

## PART II

He did not come in the dawning; he did not come at noon;
And out o' the tawny sunset, before the rise o' the moon,
When the road was a gypsy's ribbon, looping the purple moor,
A red-coat troop came marching—
    Marching—marching—
King George's men came marching up to the old inn-door.

They said no word to the landlord, they drank his ale instead,
But they gagged his daughter and bound her to the foot of
      her narrow bed;
Two of them knelt at her casement, with muskets at their side!
There was death at every window,
    And hell at one dark window,
For Bess could see, through her casement, the road that
      he would ride.

They had tied her up to attention, with many a sniggering jest;
They had bound a musket beside her, with the barrel beneath
      her breast!
"Now keep good watch!" and they kissed her. She heard the dead
      man say —
*Look for me by moonlight;*
    *Watch for me by moonlight;*
*I'll come to thee by moonlight, though hell should bar the way.*

---

tawny: having a warm, sandy color
muskets: rifles
sniggering: snickering; laughing in a mean, scornful way

She twisted her hands behind her; but all the knots held good!
She writhed her hands till her fingers were wet with sweat or blood!
They stretched and strained in the darkness, and the hours crawled
  by like years,
Till, now, on the stroke of midnight,
 Cold, on the stroke of midnight,
The tip of one finger touched it! The trigger at least was hers!

The tip of one finger touched it; she strove no more for the rest!
Up, she stood to attention, with the barrel beneath her breast,
She would not risk their hearing; she would not strive again;
For the road lay bare in the moonlight;
 Blank and bare in the moonlight;
And the blood of her veins in the moonlight throbbed to her
  love's refrain.

*Tlot-tlot, tlot-tlot!* Had they heard it? The horse-hoofs ringing clear;
*Tlot-tlot, tlot-tlot,* in the distance? Were they deaf that they did
  not hear?
Down the ribbon of moonlight, over the brow of the hill,
The highwayman came riding,
 Riding, riding!
The red-coats looked to their priming! She stood up, straight
  and still!

strove: tried with great effort
priming: preparations for firing a musket

*Tlot-tlot*, in the frosty silence! *Tlot-tlot*, in the echoing night!
Nearer he came and nearer! Her face was like a light!
Her eyes grew wide for a moment; she drew one last deep breath,
Then her finger moved in the moonlight,
    Her musket shattered the moonlight,
Shattered her breast in the moonlight and warned him—with
       her death.

He turned; he spurred to the westward; he did not know who stood
Bowed, with her head o'er the musket, drenched with her own
       red blood!
Not till the dawn he heard it, his face grew gray to hear
How Bess, the landlord's daughter,
    The landlord's black-eyed daughter,
Had watched for her love in the moonlight, and died in the
       darkness there.

Back, he spurred like a madman, shrieking a curse to the sky,
With the white road smoking behind him, and his rapier
       brandished high!
Blood-red were his spurs in the golden moon; wine-red was his
       velvet coat,
When they shot him down on the highway,
    Down like a dog on the highway,
And he lay in his blood in the highway, with the bunch of lace
       at his throat!

---

spurred: urged on and directed a horse (with spurs)
brandished: waved or held

*And still of a winter's night, they say, when the wind is in the trees,*
*When the moon is a ghostly galleon tossed upon cloudy seas,*
*When the road is a ribbon of moonlight over the purple moor,*
*A highwayman comes riding—*
    *Riding—riding—*
*A highwayman comes riding, up to the old inn-door.*

*Over the cobbles he clatters and clangs in the dark inn-yard;*
*And he taps with his whip on the shutters, but all is locked*
      *and barred;*
*He whistles a tune to the window, and who should be waiting there*
    *But the landlord's black-eyed daughter,*
      *Bess, the landlord's daughter,*
*Plaiting a dark red love-knot into her long black hair.*

# STORIES OF SCIENTISTS

*The heights by great men reached and kept*
*Were not attained by sudden flight;*
*But they, while their companions slept,*
*Were toiling upward through the night.*

—Henry Wadsworth Longfellow

# MICHAEL FARADAY'S WORLD
### by Nancy Veglahn

## 1

Michael Faraday was always asking questions.

He asked so many questions because he wondered about everything. He wondered what makes people sneeze, and whether flies have bones, and why candles burn, and what keeps the stars in order. It was not easy to get answers to questions like these in Michael Faraday's part of London in the beginning of the nineteenth century. But he kept asking and wondering.

When his father heated the blacksmith's forge, Michael wondered why the iron horseshoe nails became soft when they were heated, but the anvil didn't. When his mother baked bread, he wondered how the little bit of yeast she put in the dough could make the whole loaf rise. Most of all, Michael wondered why nobody else seemed to wonder as he did. His parents were too busy wondering how to get enough money to feed their four children and pay the bills.

When he was ten years old, Michael became an errand boy for a bookbinder, Mr. Riebau. Michael also had to sweep the floors, wash the windows, and keep things tidy. He liked working in the bookbinder's shop. He liked the smells of ink and glue and leather and crisp new paper. He liked Mr. Riebau. Most of all, he liked to read.

Sometimes Michael found articles about new inventions and scientific discoveries. He read these very carefully and thought about the people who figure out how things work.

---

bookbinder: a person who sews pages and covers together to make a book

Several older boys worked in Mr. Riebau's shop and lived in his house. They were called apprentices. These boys would work for the bookbinder for seven years; then they had learned enough to become bookbinders themselves. Michael watched them helping Mr. Riebau put new covers on worn-out books. Of course, he asked a lot of questions.

One day when Michael was fourteen years old, Mr. Riebau asked him a question. "You seem to like watching us work. Wouldn't you like to move here and be an apprentice?"

Michael Faraday lived and worked at Mr. Riebau's shop for seven years. Mr. Riebau let Michael read before work, after work, at mealtime—whenever there was a spare moment. He read everything that was sent to Mr. Riebau for binding: Arabian Nights, the plays of Shakespeare, a book of sermons, a history of England, nursery rhymes, scientific studies.

One day, Michael had a chance to read the "E" volume of the Encyclopedia Britannica. There was not time to read all of it, of course. The book would only be in Mr. Riebau's shop for a few days. He had to skip over sections like "Egg" and "Egret" and "Elamite."

But when he came to the article on "Electricity," Michael read every word. That took him several hours, because it was 127 pages long. He copied much of the information into his notebook. Electricity was one of the things Michael had wondered most about.

Mr. Riebau agreed to let Michael use the back of the shop at night for scientific experiments. He also let Michael have

apprentices: people who are learning a trade from an expert
egret: a kind of bird like a heron
Elamite: an ancient language

scraps of metal, wood, and glass, and bits of glue left over from bookbinding.

The shop was quiet at night. It was a good time to work and think. Michael built up the fire in the fireplace and used it to heat chemicals and melt metals. Shadows danced on the walls and ceilings as he worked. Sometimes one of his concoctions went wrong and exploded with a "pop." Usually by the time he dragged himself up the stairs to bed he had learned something, even if it was only what not to try again.

One day Mr. Riebau was talking to a wealthy customer, a Mr. Dance, about some new scientific books. "I have a boy here who'll want to read those," Mr. Riebau said, and told Mr. Dance about his curious apprentice. He called Michael into the room.

"Have you ever gone to hear the lectures at the Royal Institution?" Mr. Dance asked.

Michael shook his head.

"A boy with your interests shouldn't miss those. Sir Humphry Davy is speaking in a few weeks."

Michael knew that Sir Humphry Davy was the greatest scientist in England, and that the Royal Institution was the place where Davy and many other scientists did their work. He also knew the lectures cost money.

Mr. Dance must have understood Michael's problem, because a few days later he came back to the bookbinder's shop with tickets to four lectures by Sir Humphry Davy.

---

concoctions: unusual mixtures

## 2

It was February, 1812. Napoleon's armies had conquered most of Europe. British soldiers were fighting the French in Spain and the Americans across the Atlantic. Michael Faraday knew all this, but he thought of nothing but the lectures.

On the night of the first lecture, he walked through lightly falling snow to Number 21 Albemarle Street. The Royal Institution was a large building of gray stone with fourteen pillars across the front. It looked as wonderful as a castle from the Arabian Nights, and as Michael walked up the wide stairs inside he felt sure there were amazing secrets hidden behind each closed door.

He found a seat in the crowded lecture hall, and soon Sir Humphry Davy appeared on the platform. As the great man spoke, Michael wrote down everything. His fingers ached, and his eyes burned from writing in the dimly lit room. He had no time to think about all the facts and theories Davy talked about. He would do that later.

In the next few weeks Michael copied the notes into a fresh notebook he had made. He drew pictures to show the equipment Davy had used on the platform and the experiments he had done. There was another lecture in March and two in April. Michael took careful notes on all of them.

The finished notebook with its pictures was 386 pages long. It was full of facts about chemicals and gases and steam engines and the laws of nature.

But still Michael had questions. He had more questions than ever.

His years as Mr. Riebau's apprentice were almost over. In a few months he would be ready to go and work as a "journeyman" bookbinder. It was a good trade, and he liked it. Yet he could not forget the Royal Institution

Faraday had a daring idea. Why not ask Sir Humphry whether there might be work for him at the Institution? Why not send him those lecture notes to show him that Michael Faraday could listen and learn? He put the notes in a neat package, included a letter, and sent the bundle to Sir Humphry Davy.

Months crawled by with no answer. Michael began to lose hope for the first time. He was twenty-two years old, a grown man with no money and no education except what he had found for himself. Maybe it was silly to dream of becoming a scientist.

One night early in 1813, Michael was getting ready for bed when he heard someone knocking loudly at the door. He looked out the window and saw a fancy carriage in the street. When he opened the door, he was even more startled to see a footman in a powdered wig and a coat with bright brass buttons. The man handed him a note. Michael was too surprised to say anything, and the footman got back into the carriage and drove away. Using a coal from the fire, Michael lit a candle and looked at the note. It was addressed to him.

Sir Humphry Davy wanted Michael Faraday to call the next morning at the Royal Institution.

After a sleepless night, Michael put on his best suit and walked to the big stone building in Albemarle Street. A doorman directed him to the office of Sir Humphry.

"I had to fire one of our laboratory assistants yesterday," Davy told him. "Got into a fight—the man was a troublemaker from the beginning. I need a helper to keep my

---

journeyman: a person who has learned a trade but is not yet a master

equipment in order and write up the records and perhaps even help me prepare for experiments. I remembered your letter and those amazing notes you took on my lectures...."

The salary would be a guinea a week, plus fuel, candles, and aprons. Best of all, Michael could live in the Royal Institution; there was a room available on the top floor. Michael made a bundle of his few extra clothes, his notebook, and other belongings. He left his homemade laboratory equipment behind; he would have better things to work with at the Royal Institution. A charwoman showed him to his room that evening. The roof slanted over his head, and the windows were small and dusty. All the furniture he needed was there: a narrow bed, a desk, some wooden chairs.

In the middle of the night, Michael was still awake, his heart thudding with excitement. He got up and lit a candle. Then he pulled his clothes on and crept down the stairs, through the wide hall, and into the laboratory where he was to work with Sir Humphry Davy.

Sir Humphry had shown the room to him earlier, but it looked different at night. The faint candle glow showed hints of the wonders of that room: gleaming glass jars and bright metal tools and mysterious chemicals stored on shelves that reached from floor to ceiling. A mixture of powerful smells made Michael's nose twitch. He would have to get used to all those chemical odors; they were even stronger than the smells of the bookbinding shop. A bit of hot wax stung his thumb. He looked down at the candle and wondered suddenly how it worked. He had been using candles all his life, but he had never noticed before that the flame was brighter at the top and bottom than in the middle. Why was

guinea: a gold coin once used in Britain
charwoman: a cleaning woman

that? He went back upstairs, climbed into bed, and fell asleep thinking about candles.

He started work in the wonderful laboratory the next morning. At first he only washed and dried the equipment and learned where everything was. But soon Sir Humphry let him help with the experiments themselves, and Michael began to feel like a scientist at last.

He did so well as Davy's assistant that he was soon promoted to "Assistant and Superintendent of the Apparatus of the Laboratory and Mineralogical Collection." This long title meant that he could now do some of his own experiments as well as help the senior scientists.

## 3

It was an exciting time to be a scientist. All over the world discoveries were being made about the laws of nature. Each new discovery led to more experiments and more discoveries.

Michael Faraday was fascinated by magnets and electricity. He filled notebooks with accounts of experiments using magnets, wires, and batteries. Most of these experiments didn't work as he expected, but he kept trying.

He was not the only scientist trying to learn more about electricity. An Italian, Alessandro Volta, had discovered how to make a simple battery that produced small amounts of electricity from chemicals. A Frenchman, André Ampère, invented a device called a galvanometer, which could measure electric power. And in 1825, William Sturgeon made an electromagnet. He bent an iron bar into a horseshoe shape, wrapped it with copper wire, and sent an electric current

apparatus: equipment
mineralogical: having to do with minerals

through the wire. This turned the iron horseshoe into a powerful magnet that could hold as much as nine pounds of metal. As long as electric current went through the wire, the iron horseshoe was an electromagnet. When the current was turned off, it was just a piece of iron wrapped with wire.

Magnetism could be generated by electricity. And so, Michael Faraday wondered, why couldn't electricity be generated by magnetism?

No one was able to do it. Wires were wrapped around magnets in every possible way, but the magnets did not make any electric current.

Faraday built a tiny model: an iron bar an inch long wrapped in a spiral of copper wire. He carried it in his vest pocket. When he was at a boring committee meeting or a long dinner party, he would take the model from his pocket and stare at it. What was the answer?

He believed that everything in the world worked together in ways that made sense, if people could only understand. The energy of lightning, of sparks, of magnetism and electricity, was the same energy in different forms. He was only trying to change the energy from one form to another.

One summer morning in 1831, Faraday sat at his workbench in the laboratory, writing down the story of another failure. He had wrapped a large bar-shaped magnet with wire, but nothing had happened. It didn't seem to matter how powerful the magnet was; it would not make an electric current.

Then he stopped and looked at the round lip of a glass beaker he was using. A circle! What if the magnet were round?

He had one of his helpers make a circle of soft iron. Faraday wrapped a coil of copper wire around one side of it. He called this Wire A. Around the other side of the ring he wrapped another wire, Wire B, which he attached to a galvanometer.

He then fastened Wire A to a small battery, sending an electrical charge through it, which made the iron ring into an electromagnet. He hoped that this would cause a current to flow in the second wire, the one that was not connected to the battery.

The needle on the galvanometer moved, showing a charge in Wire B. It fell back immediately, but the needle moved again when Faraday disconnected Wire A from the battery.

Faraday stared at the galvanometer. Had it moved showing an electric current in Wire B—or was he imagining it? He connected the battery to Wire A again; the needle moved again. But the moment he pulled the Wire A connection away, the needle fell back. It moved when he moved Wire A.

The experiment seemed to show that electricity could be generated from magnetism. But Faraday was not satisfied. As usual, the answer he found only raised more questions. Why wasn't the current steady? Why did the electrical charge in Wire B show up only when he connected or disconnected the battery to Wire A? Why did the needle always swing back?

Faraday spent the next three weeks thinking about it. He wrote in a letter to a friend, "I am busy just now again on electromagnetism, and think I have got hold of a good thing, but can't say."

He repeated the experiment, using wires and magnets in many different shapes and sizes. He discovered that all he had to do was to move an electromagnet close to a coil of wire and the needle would jump.

The important thing was motion! It was a moving magnet that could generate electric power. Faraday had his answer.

Many years later, this idea was used by others to build a machine called a dynamo. It is the dynamo that generates the power to run our modern washing machines and television sets and electric ovens. Faraday called the discovery that made the dynamo possible "magnetoelectric induction."

"But what's the use of it?" people would ask Faraday when he told them about making electric current from magnetism.

He liked to quote the answer Benjamin Franklin had given when asked a similar question: "What's the use of a baby?" Franklin had said. "Some day it will grow up."

## 4

"Think about how wonderful it is to live, to stand up and move about." Michael Faraday looked from the stage of the auditorium of the Royal Institution to the rows and rows of young faces in the audience. "Yet most people don't wonder about these things. They might think a mountain was wonderful, or a waterfall, but not the fact that they can walk around in the daytime and lie down at night."

induction: the way in which a conductor receives an electrical current from a magnetic field

It was Christmastime. Faraday had started a new tradition at the Royal Institution. Every year during the Christmas holidays, he gave lectures about science to the children who were on vacation from school. They crowded into the auditorium to hear Faraday. Even the Prince of Wales, the future King of England, came to the Christmas lectures.

Once Faraday put an ordinary candle on his desk and asked questions, just as he had always asked questions of everything. What makes a candle burn? Why is the flame always brighter toward the top? Where does the candle go when it has burned down to a stump? Why does its light go out if you put it under a glass jar? Why do some candles smoke a great deal and others very little?

Usually he told the children about some kind of experiment that they could do at home. After the lecture on candles, he told them to take a cold spoon and hold it over the flame of a candle. The spoon would then get a sort of mist over it. That showed that one of the products of a burning candle is water.

Sometimes Faraday had his desk piled with things the audience could take home and work with: bits of rock, pieces of wire, metals, and harmless chemicals. When he talked about static electricity, he told them how they could make a static electricity generator out of a piece of sealing wax, a watch, and a small wooden board.

One morning, as Faraday left the Royal Institution to take a walk through the cold, damp air, two young boys saw him and whispered to each other. Finally one of them said shyly, "Good morning, Mr. Faraday."

Michael Faraday smiled and said, "Good morning. May I ask how you gentlemen know my name?"

"We went to your Christmas lectures, sir," said the boy who had spoken before.

"All of them," the second boy grinned.

"We wondered if you'd tell us what the Christmas lectures will be about this year, sir," the first one said.

"I haven't decided yet," Faraday told them. "Perhaps they might have something to do with electricity."

"Oh, that would be first-rate!" said the second boy.

They thanked him and raced off, beaming. "Ask questions," he called after them. "Never stop asking questions!"

# NIKOLA TESLA, INVENTOR
*by Shawn Lake*

Nikola Tesla stood on the darkened stage with his hands on his hips and looked out at his audience. His white tuxedo seemed to shimmer in the dim light, and he was so tall and thin that he appeared to be walking on stilts. The year was 1891, and people filled every seat and stood in the aisles to listen to this elegant man with bright, blue eyes talk about electricity.

On tables nearby lay a dozen glass tubes that gave off an eerie glow. As Tesla stepped forward, the lights cast his shadow along the walls. He held up his hands to signal for silence. The audience leaned forward in their seats as he began to speak. In his careful, accented English, he told them about light bulbs and lightning, waterfalls and power, and how electricity was about to change everyone's future.

But Tesla had more than words in store for his audience. Taking hold of a wire, he spread his arms as tens of thousands of volts of electric power passed over his body. Streamers of blue light flowed over him, and sparks flew from his fingertips. When he picked up a long, glass tube, it began to glow. Tesla himself was the conductor of enough electricity to light up the bulb.

Nikola Tesla sounds like a nineteenth century sideshow performer, but he was one of the most brilliant inventors in history. In fact, every electrical appliance today uses at least one of Tesla's inventions.

---

conductor: something that allows an electrical current to flow through it

If you had seen him striding down the street, though, you would never have thought that he spent most of his time building inventions in a laboratory. He looked more like a diplomat, with his tidy white shirt buttoned at the throat and his hair slicked back. If you had happened to sit by him in a restaurant, you would have thought he was a bit odd. Tesla always ate as though he were at a formal dinner, with each cup and plate in its place. He had been afraid of germs since he was a boy, and he used stacks of napkins—preferably 18, a number divisible by 3, another one of his obsessions—with each meal to clean his hands and silverware. And although he often stayed up all night working on an experiment, he always tried to be alert the next day.

Tesla wasn't the only inventor staying up all night. Before the discoveries of the late 1800s, people still depended on oil lamps and steam engines. Dozens of inventors throughout the world were racing to be the first to create a dependable light bulb, send power from one city to another, and transmit messages without wires. It was a tangled and disorderly process, with each inventor building on the discoveries of others.

Nikola Tesla raced with the others, but he was usually one step ahead of them. Born at midnight between 9 and 10 July 1856 in Smiljan, Croatia, Tesla was, from his boyhood, able to solve complicated problems in his head. He called his mind his mental blackboard and he would use it to work out the details of an invention and then put it to use in real life. Tesla

---

obsessions: ideas or habits that become an unhealthy and excessive focus
dependable: reliable
disorderly: having no set rules or structure

even boasted of his early forays into inventing, "I needed no models, drawings, or experiments. I could picture them all as real in my mind."

Tesla had a good model for his creative mind. His mother invented kitchen tools and was famous for the fine needlework and weaving she did on a loom she designed herself. Tesla followed her example for original thinking. When he was very young, he caught frogs with a fishing rod he designed and built, complete with hook and line. He also built a motor powered by June bugs and experimented with a flying machine. When he saw a picture of Niagara Falls, he imagined a big wheel run by water like the ones he built in the creek near his home. The challenge to create a waterwheel that would harness and generate the awesome force of water flowing over Niagara Falls stayed with Tesla until he was an adult.

And Tesla could never pass up a challenge. When he was at college in Austria, he saw that the DC (direct current) electric motors people used then were inefficient and noisy. These motors sparked and rattled because they used a moving part called a commutator to convert electricity from the wires into the motion of a spinning shaft. Tesla told his professor that he could invent an AC (alternating current) motor that would work without a commutator, and the professor laughed at him, calling it "an impossible idea. Mr. Tesla may accomplish great things," the professor said, "but he will never do this."

---

forays: attempts
harness: to rein in; to collect
generate: to bring about or produce
inefficient: wasteful of energy or resources
commutator: a series of metal bars that, as part of an electrical generator, produce direct current
shaft: a pole

But Tesla believed it could be done, and though he went on to other projects, he kept thinking about the AC motor. Just as he did when he was a boy, Tesla built the experiments in his mind instead of on a workbench. But one day in 1882 while he was walking in a park with a friend, the answer came to him as, he said, "a flash of lightning, and in an instant the truth was revealed."

On his mental blackboard, Tesla saw the spinning shaft of a motor powered by two out-of-step alternating currents, with no need for a commutator. Other inventors had solved parts of the problem, but no one had visualized a complete AC motor. Tesla was so excited that he grabbed a stick and drew a diagram in the dirt to explain the machine to his friend.

All generators make electricity by spinning the positive and negative poles of a magnet past a coiled wire, and the current they produce is alternating—that is, it jumps back and forth between positive and negative many times a second. Early scientists believed that such a current was useless, so they designed motors that changed it. These first motors used commutators that moved back and forth between the magnetic poles. Commutators switched the current so that it flowed only in one direction, thereby creating direct current. But commutators sparked and clattered as they worked.

Tesla's diagram—and his invention—took the alternating current from two different wires instead of just one. By timing the currents in the wires so they were out of step with each other, he used them to spin the shaft the way two legs pedaling a bicycle can spin the wheels. This eliminated the commutator and made the motors run more quietly and safely. Tesla patented the first of his AC motors in 1890, and today nearly all electric motors are based on his invention.

When he was still a young man, Tesla went to the United States to work for Thomas Edison in his New Jersey laboratory. By that time, 1884, Edison was already famous for a number of inventions, including the incandescent light bulb.

Edison immediately gave Tesla the job of repairing the DC generators used to power a large ship. Tesla not only did the job overnight, but he also told Edison that he could redesign the generators so that they would work better and save money. Edison was impressed by Tesla's work, but when Tesla tried to convince him that AC generators would work better than DC, Edison got angry, saying, "Spare me that nonsense. We're set up for direct current in America."

Edison was the opposite of Tesla in almost every way, and they soon came to dislike each other. While Tesla was neat and dignified, Edison often slept in his lab for days at a time, and his clothes were rumpled and dirty. Edison had a large home and family, while Tesla believed such things would distract him, and he never married. Tesla cared little for the business side of inventing, but Edison was a shrewd bargainer when it came to contracts and payments. Tesla was proud of his university degree while Edison was entirely self-educated. His method of invention was trial and error, which Tesla considered slow and inefficient. "If Edison had a needle to find in a haystack," Tesla said, "he would proceed at once with the diligence of the bee to examine straw after straw until he found the object of his search."

With all these differences, it was difficult for the two inventors to get along, and after a disagreement about payment for his work, Tesla walked out. The biggest dispute

incandescent: glowing as a result of intense heat
diligence: careful attention
dispute: an argument

they had, however, was over electric power itself. Edison's bulbs operated on DC power, while Tesla believed that AC was the way of the future. Edison already operated the Edison Electric Company, which generated DC power for a small number of houses and factories in New York City, and Tesla soon opened the Tesla Electric Company to develop an AC power system. When investors chose sides and tried to convince the public that their way was better, a "battle of the currents" began.

Today we know that AC power is better for large users like cities while DC works best in batteries. Tesla was correct when he pointed out that DC could only be transmitted a few miles before the lights grew dim. AC could travel over hundreds of miles of wire and still light a home. In the end the facts won out, and AC power runs our cities and industries today.

Like most inventors, Tesla often solved parts of a problem, and others took his work further. While still at Edison's lab, he worked on an idea for creating light through a gas instead of a filament, and that idea became the fluorescent lights we use today. Tesla was able to send wireless transmissions—soon to be known as radio—in 1893, and the inventor Guglielmo Marconi later used his ideas to build a device that sent a radio signal across the Atlantic Ocean.

Although Tesla was one of the most famous people in the world at the turn of the century, and though he received many honors for his work, his name was often left out of early books and articles by scientists, usually because Tesla was careless about applying for patents and signing contracts with the manufacturers of his inventions. He had little patience with those who thought only of money.

filament: a small wire that glows when an electrical current passes through it

But some of Tesla's ideas seemed so bizarre that people
decided they shouldn't believe in his work. He built a
laboratory in Colorado where he tried to generate one
hundred million volts of electricity in order to use what he
called the earth's "resonant frequency" to send signals
around the world without wires. He even said that if the
inhabitants of Mars knew how to receive his signals, he could

talk to them, too. At one point, he sent lightning bolts 135 feet in the air, and the nearby city of Colorado Springs went dark when he shorted out their power system.

Tesla could also be arrogant and impatient with people he worked with, and some newspaper reporters called him crazy and unreliable. But there was a little truth in even his most outrageous ideas, and his peculiar personality was the flip side of his genius. Tesla laughed at his critics.

"The present is theirs," Tesla said. "The future, for which I really worked, is mine."

*Today Tesla's achievements speak for themselves. AC power, the system the world runs on today, uses motors and generators based on Tesla's inventions. If you visit Niagara Falls, you will see that he fulfilled his childhood dream of the waterwheel. His name appears nine times on the dedication plaque there, for nine separate inventions used in his great AC dynamos. The tesla, a unit of magnetic induction, is named for him. And every TV and radio uses a device called a Tesla coil that boosts the household current. This same device is also used for Hollywood special effects, like the blue lightning arching up the buzzing metal coil in Frankenstein movies. His work with electricity and magnetism formed some of the building blocks for lasers, radar, fax machines, and electron microscopes.*

---

arrogant: conceited; full of oneself

# HEALING A WOUNDED HEART: DANIEL HALE WILLIAMS
### by William Orem

Chicago, 1893, a quiet summer evening—a man, his face clenched in agony, his shirt stained with blood, stumbles through the doors of Provident Hospital.

Fortunately for the wounded man, who was black, this hospital gave care to patients of any color—which was more than could be said of many of the hospitals in the city, indeed, in the whole United States.

Provident Hospital had been founded in 1891 by Dr. Daniel Hale Williams. Williams himself had come a long way before founding the hospital. He was born in Pennsylvania in 1856, before the Civil War, at a time when almost four million African Americans in the United States were still slaves. Daniel's parents, however, were not slaves. His father owned a barbershop. As a boy, Daniel started to learn the shoemaking trade. Later, he worked in barbershops as well. All the while, he studied hard and read constantly in order to learn all that he could.

As a young man, Daniel Hale Williams worked as an apprentice to a well-respected surgeon, Dr. Henry Palmer. This apprenticeship prepared Williams to enter Chicago Medical School, one of the best medical schools in the nation at the time. After three years of hard work, Williams graduated with his M.D. degree in 1883.

---

clenched: held tightly
M.D.: *Medicinae Doctor* (Latin) = Doctor of Medicine

When Dr. Williams set up his medical practice, there were only three other black doctors in Chicago. He worked at the South Side Dispensary, where he was often called upon to make use of his skills in surgery. He also provided medical care for children at a nearby orphanage and taught anatomy at the medical college where he had studied.

Wherever he looked, Dr. Williams saw few opportunities for African Americans to enter medical professions. He also saw that black people were sometimes refused medical care, or did not receive the same quality of care available to white people. That is why, when the Reverend Louis Reynolds came to him with an idea, Dr. Williams saw the wisdom of it. They would start their own hospital—a place where black people could get the same quality treatment as white people. The hospital would also serve as a training school for nurses—a goal dear to the heart of Reverend Reynolds, whose sister wanted to become a nurse but had been rejected from existing schools simply because she was black.

dispensary: a place where medicine or medical treatment is given out
anatomy: the scientific study of the parts and structures of living things

With support from other clergymen, wealthy donors, and community residents, Provident Hospital opened its doors in May of 1891. It gave patients equal access to quality care, and doctors and nurses equal access to quality training. In fact, Provident was the first hospital in the United States in which black and white doctors worked together to care for all patients, regardless of race.

On the summer night that the man with the knife wound stumbled into Provident Hospital, Dr. Williams was called in. The doctor reassured the patient with his calm, dignified manner. Williams was confident that he could help. But then he saw the wound—it went deep into the chest, perhaps into the heart.

At this time, the X-ray machine had not been invented, so there was no way for Dr. Williams to look inside the patient to determine the extent of the injury. No way, that is, except to open the man's chest and look right into it.

Open the chest? In 1893, doctors operated on torn muscles, on broken bones, even on serious knife wounds to other parts of the body. But they did not perform heart surgery. Many doctors argued that it was too dangerous; they said a surgeon would be foolish even to try such a thing.

Yes, it was dangerous. But Daniel Hale Williams was not foolish—on the contrary, he was very careful. He knew that, unless he took this risk, the patient was almost sure to die.

With several other doctors observing and assisting, Dr. Williams started the operation. He cut into the man's chest. He cut even deeper. He examined the depth of the stab wound. He found and repaired a torn blood vessel. He stitched up the pericardium, a fluid-filled bag that surrounds the heart. He very carefully cleaned the wound and the chest cavity, to make sure that no infection set in. Then he stitched closed the man's chest, again taking great care to keep everything as antiseptic as he could.

The surgery was a success. The wounded man lived, not only for the rest of that day, or the rest of that week, but for decades afterward. Dr. Williams had given him back his life. In the process, he became the first doctor to perform successful heart surgery.

Dr. Williams wasn't trying to become a hero on that evening in 1893, nor could he have known he was going to become famous for his accomplishment. But the newspapers let the world know, in dramatic headlines that read, "SEWED UP HIS HEART!"

Dr. Williams went on to become chief surgeon at the Freedman's Hospital in Washington, D.C. He reorganized the hospital and made it into a model of high quality medical care.

Daniel Hale Williams was successful in many ways. He worked hard to become a doctor at a time when the doors of the medical profession were generally closed to African Americans. He remained committed to his belief that all people deserve quality health care. And as a surgeon, he was bold enough to take risks but careful enough to ensure the safety of his patients.

---

antiseptic: free of germs
ensure: to guarantee or make sure

# MARIE CURIE AND THE DISCOVERY OF RADIOACTIVITY

*by Mara Rockliff*

"**M**arie! It's here!" shouted Pierre. "Our shipment has arrived!"

Marie Curie did not even pause to grab her hat. She rushed out into the street after her husband. There it was—a big, heavy wagon, like the ones that brought much-needed coal for their lab's dilapidated stove. But this wagon carried a far more precious and exciting load.

A moment later, people passing by the School of Physics and Chemistry were treated to a sight not often seen on the fashionable streets of Paris in the early 1900s: a bareheaded young woman in a laboratory smock, ripping eagerly into the pile of heavy sacks and burying her hands in… *dirt?*

To the Austrian mine owners who had sent the pitchblende ore, it was just dirt. After all, they had already taken out the valuable part—the metallic element called uranium—and dumped what was left over in a nearby pine forest. If a pair of eccentric French scientists wanted them to scoop up the worthless stuff and ship it, the mine owners were happy to oblige.

---

dilapidated: run-down; neglected and in poor condition
physics: a branch of science concerned with the relationship between matter and energy
pitchblende: a brownish-black mineral that is uncommonly high in radioactive elements
ore: rock or mineral from which a valuable element may be extracted
eccentric: odd; unusual in one's behavior
oblige: to help

But Marie and Pierre Curie knew the secret of the dull brown ore. Hidden deep within it was a new chemical element. No one, the Curies included, had ever seen this element. Still, the husband-and-wife team had given it a name: radium. And Marie was determined to prove radium was real.

No one knew how difficult the task would be. But Marie, although still a student, had already shown that she possessed the most important quality of a successful scientist. When it came to the search for knowledge, she never gave up.

When she was growing up in Russian-occupied Poland, even to study science was forbidden. Many nights, young Maria Sklodowska (as she was then named) slipped through the dark streets of Warsaw on her way to an illegal night school, glancing anxiously over her shoulder for any sign of the Russian police. Days, she worked teaching children, saving her rubles to send her older sister to medical school in the city of intellectual freedom—Paris, France.

At last, her own turn came. Her sister, newly married, sent for Marie to join her in Paris. Clutching a blanket and a folding chair—the fourth-class train ticket, all she could afford, did not provide even a seat—she hugged the rest of her family goodbye. When Marie arrived in Paris in 1891, she studied physics at the greatest university in Europe, the Sorbonne. But how poor she was! And how poorly prepared! She barely knew enough French, let alone advanced math and science, to understand the lectures.

Marie studied late into the evenings in the library, struggling to catch up with her classmates. Then she climbed the six flights to her little room. In the winter, it was so cold that she emptied her closet, piling the clothes on her bed so she'd be warm enough to sleep. Sometimes she had no money to buy even an egg or a loaf of bread. But then, how could she take the time to stop studying long enough to cook?

Her hard work was rewarded. Marie won her degree in physics, graduating first in her class. And the next year she earned a second degree, in mathematics. She also met the man who soon became her husband—Pierre Curie, a brilliant young physicist as promising (and as poor) as Marie. Their love for each other was equaled only by their shared love of science.

It was a thrilling time to be a scientist. The year the Curies were married, 1895, a German physicist named Wilhelm Roentgen discovered a new kind of ray that could be used to "see" inside people and photograph their bones. He called them X rays. The X stood for "unknown."

Not long after, the French physicist Henri Becquerel discovered that uranium let out another type of ray. These rays were weak compared to X rays, and even Becquerel himself did not think his discovery of much importance. But Marie found the rays fascinating. Where did they come from? How were they produced? She decided to examine these mysterious "Becquerel rays" for her advanced research.

She set to work. Day after day, Marie experimented with uranium under all kinds of conditions: dry and wet; powdered and solid; pure and mixed with other elements. She heated the uranium, and shone lights on it. Then, using a special instrument called an electrometer, which Pierre and his brother had invented, she measured the uranium rays and carefully copied the numbers down in her notebook.

The results were astonishing. It didn't seem to matter what she did to the uranium. Nothing affected the strength of the rays—nothing but the amount of uranium present. The energy appeared to come from inside the metal itself, deep down at the level of its atoms. Marie named this atomic energy *radioactivity.* A substance that emitted this energy was called *radioactive.*

Her experiments yielded a second surprise. A sample of uranium-rich pitchblende turned out to be three or four times as radioactive as pure uranium. How could this be? Marie had already tested every known element in pitchblende. None was radioactive. But something in that pitchblende, something besides the uranium, was sending out rays.

There could only be one answer. If the extra radioactivity could not be coming from any known element, it must be coming from an *unknown* element.

Pierre was so excited by Marie's discovery that he dropped his own research on crystals to assist her. They knew the new element, which they decided to call radium, must be extremely tiny to have escaped notice all these years. Maybe it made up as little of the pitchblende as one percent! And yet this tiny bit of radium gave off stronger rays than a much larger amount of uranium. It must be powerfully radioactive.

The mine owners had sent them seven tons of pitchblende. Somewhere in that seven tons, Pierre and Marie were convinced, they would find radium.

It was like searching for a needle in a very large haystack—except that they had no way of knowing what this "needle" even looked like. And the needle would turn out to be much smaller than either of them imagined. It was not one percent. It was less than one *millionth* of one percent.

No one paid the Curies to do this work. They could not even persuade the School of Physics, where Pierre taught, to let them use a laboratory. Instead, they were forced to set up shop in an abandoned shed.

A visitor once described the Curies' laboratory as "a cross between a stable and a potato cellar." In summer, the heat was stifling. In winter, the old stove barely gave out enough warmth to thaw their frozen hands. The roof leaked when it rained.

"Yet," Marie would write years later, "it was in this miserable old shed that we passed the best and happiest years of our life, devoting our entire days to our work."

The work could be backbreaking. Marie spent many hours boiling down pitchblende in enormous pots, stirring the heavy mixture with an iron rod as tall as she was, gasping and coughing from the fumes. Later, she faced the nearly impossible task of producing purer and purer samples in the drafty, dusty shed with its dirt floor.

A year, two years, three years. Marie edged closer to her goal. Sometimes, in the evenings, she and Pierre put their little daughter to bed, leaving her in the care of her grandfather. Then the couple would walk arm in arm through the Paris streets, returning to their darkened laboratory to gaze at the old wooden tables full of tubes and bottles glowing with a faint blue light.

Finally, one day in 1902, they were able to make their announcement to the world. Marie and Pierre Curie had a pure sample of a new element called radium, thousands of times more radioactive than uranium. And it was useful. While Marie had labored to purify radium, Pierre had been experimenting with her samples. He discovered that radium could kill cancer cells. Compared to surgery or to chemicals

---

stifling: extremely stuffy, hot, and uncomfortable

used to treat cancer at the time, radium was much safer and more effective.

Radium rapidly became big business. A single gram was worth $100,000. Manufacturers made their fortunes making and selling radium, using the methods Marie had developed. But Marie and Pierre refused to charge a penny for their discovery. They believed that the true spirit of science meant sharing knowledge freely.

The discovery of radioactivity would turn out to be useful in many ways. For example, among other things, doctors now use radioactive dyes to help diagnose medical problems, and scientists can use radioactivity to determine the age of fossils.

In 1903 Marie became Doctor Marie Curie. The professors who judged her work—outstanding scientists themselves—told her that no advanced research had ever made such a great contribution to science.

Later that same year, she earned an even higher honor for her research. Along with Henri Becquerel, the Curies were awarded the Nobel Prize for physics. Marie Curie became the first woman ever to win a Nobel Prize.

She would go on to win a second Nobel Prize, in chemistry, making her the first person ever to be awarded the Nobel Prize twice. And the Sorbonne made her its first female professor. But all these "firsts" meant little to Marie Curie. For her, what came first was always science.

# ENRICO FERMI:
# THE "ITALIAN NAVIGATOR"
### by Dorothy Haas

*On a gray December day in 1942, a strange telephone call was
made between Chicago and Cambridge, Massachusetts. Dr. Arthur
Compton, director of the Manhattan Project, was calling Dr. James
B. Conant, chairman of the National Defense Research Committee.
Because the United States was at war, they spoke in a kind of code.
Nobody listening in could have understood them. But Dr. Conant
knew of secret experiments being carried out in Chicago. He
understood.*

*"I have just left the Italian navigator," said Dr. Compton. "He
has arrived safely on the shores of the new world."*

*There was a tension-packed pause at the other end of the wire.
"Oh?" said Dr. Conant after a minute. "And how did he find the
natives?"*

*"Friendly!" said Dr. Compton happily. "Most friendly!"*

**A** scholarly-looking man hurried down Ellis Avenue on
Chicago's south side. An icy wind whipped winter's first
snowflakes about him. But he stepped out briskly, breathing
deeply of the cold air. Dr. Enrico Fermi—physicist, university
professor, Nobel Prize winner—enjoyed the outdoors.

He turned in at a big stone entrance built like an old
castle. It was the west gate of Stagg Field, the University of
Chicago's unused football stadium. Inside, he made his way
to a building that sat huddled beneath the deserted
west stands.

Once the building had been a squash court. It had echoed with the *squash!* sound of a little black ball and the excited calls of the boys who played there. But the building was a squash court no longer. Now it was called the "Metallurgical Laboratory." The scientists who worked there were sworn to absolute secrecy. Their mysterious experiments had nothing at all to do with the science of metals. The squash-court laboratory had become a top secret division of a United States Government agency called the Manhattan Project.

The scientist paused in the hallway of the building. He slipped out of his overcoat and shrugged into a lab coat that was streaked with black. Then he turned toward the lab. A young man was just coming out. He too wore a grimy lab coat. And he had been handling something black, as the smudges on his cheek gave proof. Whatever the experiments going on in the little building, one thing was certain—they were dirty!

Seeing his chief, the young man stopped. "Morning, Doctor," he said. He nodded down at a bottle he carried. "They're mixing the cadmium solution over at the lab right now. It'll be ready when you need it."

"And the checklist?" asked Dr. Fermi.

"That's ready too," the young man said. "It's with your things up in the gallery."

He moved on. Dr. Fermi went on into his laboratory—into a forbidding, dusky scene.

The walls of the room were black. The floor was black. At one end of the room, surrounded by a boxlike wooden framework, was a big black ball, flattened on top. The ball

---

metallurgical: having to do with metals and their properties
cadmium: a bluish-white metallic element
gallery: a room or balcony from which people watch an event

was made of graphite, the material commonly found in lead pencils. It was dust from the graphite ball that had turned everything in the laboratory an eerie black.

But never mind the dust! That graphite ball—the scientists called it a "pile"—was going to do something that few men believed possible. It was going to split the atom!

Atoms might be called the building blocks of all matter. The chairs we sit in, the food we eat, the water we drink, the air we breathe, the clothes we wear—all are made up of atoms. But atoms cannot be seen. They are almost the tiniest particles imaginable.

Imagine that you have an iron ball, one that can be cut in half as easily as an apple. Then suppose you cut one of these two pieces in half. Imagine that you keep on dividing the ball in this way, always taking one piece and cutting it in half. At last nothing would remain but a single, tiny invisible speck of iron—an atom. Imagine that you can see this atom.

You would find it made up of several parts, all of them constantly moving. The parts are called protons, neutrons, and electrons. The protons and neutrons form the core, the nucleus, of the atom. The electrons spin around the nucleus at an amazing speed. The parts of the atom are held together by an enormous strength. Try as you might, you couldn't cut the last atom of the iron ball in half.

Scientists had known of atoms and this hidden strength for many years. They had often talked about how wonderful it would be if the tremendous energy holding the atom together could be set free for man's use. But they had always thought that it would take more energy to split the atom than could be obtained from the division. Then, late in the nineteen thirties, certain discoveries were made, discoveries that shed light on the inner workings of the atom.

One man in particular thought the atom could be split to obtain unheard-of amounts of energy. He was Dr. Enrico Fermi, an Italian physicist. Dr. Fermi had come to live in the United States when he found that he was no longer able to live under a fascist form of government.

Dr. Fermi had done much work on the neutron. This work had won the Nobel Prize for him. It was work that led directly to the building of the first atomic pile at the University of Chicago.

Neutrons, said Dr. Fermi, could be made to shoot into the cores of atoms, splitting them apart. Furthermore, he said that once the process started, the neutrons set free would act upon other atoms, releasing still more energy and even more neutrons. He called this process "self-sustaining chain reaction."

The scientist faced many problems in trying to split the atom. But one problem stood out above all the others. Neutrons moved with lightning speed. A way had to be found to slow them down in their headlong flight. Otherwise they would fly off and be lost before they did their atom-splitting work.

The scientists tested many materials that they hoped might slow down the neutrons. At last Dr. Fermi thought he had the answer.

"Pure graphite should slow down the neutrons," he said. "Let us make a pile of graphite and uranium. When we have built it to just the right size, more neutrons will be trapped within the pile than can escape from it. When that happens, neutrons will begin splitting the uranium atoms and will continue to do so in a chain reaction."

---

fascist: relating to a kind of government that denies freedom and is
    usually run buy a dictator
uranium: a radioactive metallic element

Materials were hard to find. Ordinary graphite was plentiful enough. But absolutely pure graphite had to be made. And that took time. Furthermore, uranium was very scarce.

Materials arrived slowly at the laboratory. But arrive they did. At last, in the spring of 1942, the scientists were able to begin. They piled up the graphite and uranium around a source of free neutrons that would set off the pile. Then they tested it with sensitive instruments.

Yes, Dr. Fermi decided, they seemed to be on the right track. But their pile had to be bigger; too many neutrons were still escaping from it. They took down the small pile. In the fall of 1942 they began another, a bigger, one.

The materials were placed in layers. First a layer of graphite bricks was put down. This was followed by a layer of bricks that had pieces of uranium sealed in their hollowed-out cores. Slowly that pile took shape.

At last the day came when the pile was ready to be tested. It was December 2, 1942.

Dr. Fermi walked around the pile, looking at it. The big black ball nearly touched the ceiling. He slid his hand along one of the control rods.

"In these slim rods," he thought, "lies the safety of all the people in this laboratory!"

The control rods were made of cadmium. They were thrust deep into the center of the pile. There they soaked up neutrons in much the same way sponges soak up water. When they were pulled out of the pile, the neutrons would be free to split the uranium atoms. If anything went wrong, if the pile began reacting too fast, the control rods would fall back into place. They would stop the action of the pile.

Further, a group of three young men would be seated on a platform above the pile with jugs of cadmium solution. If danger threatened, they would break the jugs. The solution would pour down into the pile. It would help the control rods soak up the neutrons.

But nothing should go wrong! Mathematics had told the scientists just how to build the pile. Mathematics had told them what would happen inside of it.

And yet... The scientists were like men who know all about flying from having studied about it in books, but who have never actually flown a plane. As atom-splitters, the scientists knew all about it from their figures, but they had never actually split an atom. The control rods were like automatic pilots, ready to take over in case of trouble.

Fermi turned to a young scientist working nearby. "Is everything ready here on the floor?" he asked.

"Ready as it'll ever be," the young man answered. "All of the rods except one will come out before we begin. I'll handle the last one myself. You just give the orders."

Satisfied that everything was running smoothly on the main floor, Dr. Fermi went up to his gallery. His instruments were placed there. They would tell him, minute by minute, what was going on inside the pile. With these instruments, he would chart a safe, steady course for the reaction that would take place inside the big pile.

The morning hours slipped away. The instruments were checked and rechecked. Everyone in the laboratory had a job. Everyone went about his work quietly and surely.

At last Dr. Fermi looked at his watch. The test could begin. All the scientists who had worked on the project crowded into the gallery. There was excited chatter.

"Keep your eye on the counters!"

"...what this will mean if..."

"...what people in the neighborhood would think if they..."

Gradually a hush settled over the group. All eyes turned to Dr. Fermi. He did not show excitement. He was calm.

"We will withdraw the last cadmium rod inches at a time," he said. "Each time we will check our instruments."

"Ready down there?" he called to the main floor.

"Ready," came the cool reply.

"Now!" commanded Dr. Fermi.

The watchers grew tense. The young scientist pulled the rod a little way out of the pile.

At once the instruments in the gallery showed what was happening inside the pile. The steady *click click click* of the counters began to sound faster. Lights flashed on the panels. The first few neutrons were shooting into uranium atoms!

Dr. Fermi watched his instruments carefully. He noted the changes they showed. He was like a ship's captain moving through dangerous, shallow waters. A ship's captain takes soundings, tests, before he moves ahead. Dr. Fermi was taking his own kind of soundings; only when the nervous clicking of the counters leveled off into a steady rhythm, showing that the way ahead was safe, did he give the order to move forward.

"All right," he said. "Pull out more of the rod."

Once again the watchers tensed. And once again they relaxed. Nothing more than a quickening of the instruments showed what was happening below.

Morning wore into afternoon. Little by little the long rod was pulled from the center of the pile. Little by little activity inside the pile increased, then leveled off. A full reaction could not take place as long as any part of the rod remained in the pile.

At last, at 3:25, the final order was given.

"The rest of the rod can now come out of the pile," said Dr. Fermi.

There was no sound in the laboratory—not from the men who watched, nor from the big pile itself. But the instruments told their story. The lights flashed the message for all to see. The counters clicked excitedly for all to hear.

Inside the black ball neutrons that had no means of escape were slamming into uranium atoms. They were splitting those atoms, releasing a new kind of energy, greater than any man had ever known.

Dr. Fermi was silent. He studied his instruments for a long time.

"You can replace the rod now," he called then, and turned to the scientists who had helped to build the pile.

"The pile created a half watt of power," he said. "The amount is really quite unimportant, as you must realize, since we can increase it at will."

He looked around him, smiling quietly. "What is really important," he said, "is that we have established something new here today—a self-sustaining chain reaction!"

Hubbub broke out in the gallery. Amid congratulations and the slapping of backs, Enrico Fermi's mind was far away. "Science has opened the doors to a wonderful new world today," he thought. "Who knows what awaits us there!"

---

hubbub: great noise and confusion

# IRONY

# CHARLES

*by Shirley Jackson*

The day my son Laurie started kindergarten he renounced corduroy overalls with bibs and began wearing blue jeans with a belt; I watched him go off the first morning with the older girl next door, seeing clearly that an era of my life was ended, my sweet-voiced nursery-school tot replaced by a long-trousered, swaggering character who forgot to stop at the corner and wave goodbye to me.

He came home the same way, the front door slamming open, his cap on the floor, and the voice suddenly become raucous shouting, "Isn't anybody *here?*"

At lunch he spoke insolently to his father, spilled his baby sister's milk, and remarked that his teacher said we were not to take the name of the Lord in vain.

"How *was* school today?" I asked, elaborately casual.

"All right," he said.

"Did you learn anything?" his father asked.

Laurie regarded his father coldly. "I didn't learn nothing," he said.

"Anything," I said. "Didn't learn anything."

"The teacher spanked a boy, though," Laurie said, addressing his bread and butter. "For being fresh," he added, with his mouth full.

---

renounced: rejected; gave up
swaggering: strutting in a bold, proud way
raucous: unpleasantly loud
insolently: rudely
elaborately: with great care; painstakingly

"What did he do?" I asked. "Who was it?"

Laurie thought. "It was Charles," he said. "He was fresh. The teacher spanked him and made him stand in a corner. He was awfully fresh."

"What did he do?" I asked again, but Laurie slid off his chair, took a cookie, and left, while his father was still saying, "See here, young man."

The next day Laurie remarked at lunch, as soon as he sat down, "Well, Charles was bad again today." He grinned enormously and said, "Today Charles hit the teacher."

"Good heavens," I said, mindful of the Lord's name, "I suppose he got spanked again?"

"He sure did," Laurie said. "Look up," he said to his father.

"What?" his father said, looking up.

"Look down," Laurie said. "Look at my thumb. Gee, you're dumb." He began to laugh insanely.

"Why did Charles hit the teacher?" I asked quickly.

"Because she tried to make him color with red crayons," Laurie said. "Charles wanted to color with green crayons so he hit the teacher and she spanked him and said nobody play with Charles but everybody did."

The third day—it was Wednesday of the first week—Charles bounced a see-saw onto the head of a little girl and made her bleed, and the teacher made him stay inside all during recess. Thursday Charles had to stand in a corner during story-time because he kept pounding his feet on the floor. Friday Charles was deprived of blackboard privileges because he threw chalk.

---

deprived: kept from having

On Saturday I remarked to my husband, "Do you think kindergarten is too unsettling for Laurie? All this toughness, and bad grammar, and this Charles boy sounds like such a bad influence."

"It'll be all right," my husband said reassuringly. "Bound to be people like Charles in the world. Might as well meet them now as later."

On Monday Laurie came home late, full of news. "Charles," he shouted as he came up the hill; I was waiting anxiously on the front steps. "Charles," Laurie yelled all the way up the hill, "Charles was bad again."

"Come right in," I said, as soon as he came close enough. "Lunch is waiting."

"You know what Charles did?" he demanded, following me through the door. "Charles yelled so in school they sent a boy in from first grade to tell the teacher she had to make Charles keep quiet, and so Charles had to stay after school. And so all the children stayed to watch him."

"What did he do?" I asked.

"He just sat there," Laurie said, climbing into his chair at the table. "Hi, Pop, y'old dust mop."

"Charles had to stay after school today," I told my husband. "Everyone stayed with him."

"What does this Charles look like?" my husband asked Laurie. "What's his other name?"

"He's bigger than me," Laurie said. "And he doesn't have any rubbers and he doesn't ever wear a jacket."

Monday night was the first Parent-Teachers meeting, and only the fact that the baby had a cold kept me from going; I wanted passionately to meet Charles's mother. On Tuesday

---

passionately: with strong emotion; enthusiastically

Laurie remarked suddenly, "Our teacher had a friend come to see her in school today."

"Charles's mother?" my husband and I asked simultaneously.

"Naaah," Laurie said scornfully. "It was a man who came and made us do exercises, we had to touch our toes. Look." He climbed down from his chair and squatted down and touched his toes. "Like this," he said. He got solemnly back into his chair and said, picking up his fork, "Charles didn't even *do* exercises."

"That's fine," I said heartily. "Didn't Charles want to do exercises?"

"Naaah," Laurie said. "Charles was so fresh to the teacher's friend he wasn't *let* do exercises."

"Fresh again?" I said.

"He kicked the teacher's friend," Laurie said. "The teacher's friend told Charles to touch his toes like I just did and Charles kicked him."

"What are they going to do about Charles, do you suppose?" Laurie's father asked him.

Laurie shrugged elaborately. "Throw him out of school, I guess," he said.

Wednesday and Thursday were routine; Charles yelled during story hour and hit a boy in the stomach and made him cry. On Friday Charles stayed after school again and so did all the other children.

With the third week of kindergarten Charles was an institution in our family; the baby was being a Charles when she cried all afternoon; Laurie did a Charles when he filled his wagon full of mud and pulled it through the kitchen; even my husband, when he caught his elbow in the telephone cord and pulled telephone, ashtray, and a bowl of flowers off the table, said, after the first minute, "Looks like Charles."

During the third and fourth weeks it looked like a reformation in Charles; Laurie reported grimly at lunch on Thursday of the third week, "Charles was so good today the teacher gave him an apple."

"What?" I said, and my husband added warily, "You mean Charles?"

"Charles," Laurie said. "He gave the crayons around and he picked up the books afterward and the teacher said he was her helper."

"What happened?" I asked incredulously.

"He was her helper, that's all," Laurie said, and shrugged.

"Can this be true, about Charles?" I asked my husband that night. "Can something like this happen?"

"Wait and see," my husband said cynically. "When you've got a Charles to deal with, this may mean he's only plotting."

He seemed to be wrong. For over a week Charles was the teacher's helper; each day he handed things out and he picked things up; no one had to stay after school.

"The P.T.A. meeting's next week again," I told my husband one evening. "I'm going to find Charles's mother there."

"Ask her what happened to Charles," my husband said. "I'd like to know."

"I'd like to know myself," I said.

On Friday of that week things were back to normal. "You know what Charles did today?" Laurie demanded at the

---

reformation: a great improvement
warily: cautiously
incredulously: with disbelief
cynically: with distrust

lunch table, in a voice slightly awed. "He told a little girl to say a word and she said it and the teacher washed her mouth out with soap and Charles laughed."

"What word?" his father asked unwisely, and Laurie said, "I'll have to whisper it to you, it's so bad." He got down off his chair and went around to his father. His father bent his head down and Laurie whispered joyfully. His father's eyes widened.

"Did Charles tell the little girl to say *that*?" he asked respectfully.

"She said it *twice*," Laurie said. "Charles told her to say it *twice*."

"What happened to Charles?" my husband asked.

"Nothing," Laurie said. "He was passing out the crayons."

Monday morning Charles abandoned the little girl and said the evil word himself three or four times, getting his mouth washed out with soap each time. He also threw chalk.

My husband came to the door with me that evening as I set out for the P.T.A. meeting. "Invite her over for a cup of tea after the meeting," he said. "I want to get a look at her."

"If only she's there," I said prayerfully.

"She'll be there," my husband said. "I don't see how they could hold a P.T.A. meeting without Charles's mother."

At the meeting I sat restlessly, scanning each comfortable matronly face, trying to determine which one hid the secret of Charles. None of them looked to me haggard enough. No one stood up in the meeting and apologized for the way her son had been acting. No one mentioned Charles.

---

awed: impressed and filled with wonder
matronly: mature and motherly
haggard: worn-out; exhausted

After the meeting I identified and sought out Laurie's kindergarten teacher. She had a plate with a cup of tea and a piece of chocolate cake; I had a plate with a cup of tea and a piece of marshmallow cake. We maneuvered up to one another cautiously and smiled.

"I've been so anxious to meet you," I said. "I'm Laurie's mother."

"We're all so interested in Laurie," she said.

"Well, he certainly likes kindergarten," I said. "He talks about it all the time."

"We had a little trouble adjusting, the first week or so," she said primly, "but now he's a fine little helper. With occasional lapses, of course."

"Laurie usually adjusts very quickly," I said. "I suppose this time it's Charles's influence."

"Charles?"

"Yes," I said, laughing, "you must have your hands full in that kindergarten, with Charles."

"Charles?" she said. "We don't have any Charles in the kindergarten."

---

maneuvered: moved with a purpose
primly: in a stiff, formally proper way

# THE GIFT OF THE MAGI
## by O. Henry

One dollar and eighty-seven cents. That was all. And sixty cents of it was in pennies. Pennies saved one and two at a time by bulldozing the grocer and the vegetable man and the butcher until one's cheeks burned with the silent imputation of parsimony that such close dealing implied. Three times Della counted it. One dollar and eighty- seven cents. And the next day would be Christmas.

There was clearly nothing to do but flop down on the shabby little couch and howl. So Della did it. Which instigates the moral reflection that life is made up of sobs, sniffles, and smiles, with sniffles predominating.

While the mistress of the home is gradually subsiding from the first stage to the second, take a look at the home. A furnished flat at $8 per week. It did not exactly beggar description, but it certainly had that word on the lookout for the mendicancy squad.

In the vestibule below was a letter-box into which no letter would go, and an electric button from which no mortal

---

imputation: accusation
parsimony: extreme care in spending money that borders on stinginess
implied: suggested
instigates: urges; pushes on
predominating: prevailing; being most frequent
subsiding: settling down
flat: an apartment
beggar description: to go beyond the power of words to describe
mendicancy: the state of being beggar
vestibule: a small hall between the front door and the interior of a home

finger could coax a ring. Also appertaining thereunto was a card bearing the name "Mr. James Dillingham Young."

The "Dillingham" had been flung to the breeze during a former period of prosperity when its possessor was being paid $30 per week. Now, when the income was shrunk to $20, though, they were thinking seriously of contracting to a modest and unassuming D. But whenever Mr. James Dillingham Young came home and reached his flat above he was called "Jim" and greatly hugged by Mrs. James Dillingham Young, already introduced to you as Della. Which is all very good.

Della finished her cry and attended to her cheeks with the powder rag. She stood by the window and looked out dully at a gray cat walking a gray fence in a gray backyard. Tomorrow would be Christmas Day, and she had only $1.87 with which to buy Jim a present. She had been saving every penny she could for months, with this result. Twenty dollars a week doesn't go far. Expenses had been greater than she had calculated. They always are. Only $1.87 to buy a present for Jim. Her Jim. Many a happy hour she had spent planning for something nice for him. Something fine and rare and sterling—something just a little bit near to being worthy of the honor of being owned by Jim.

There was a pier-glass between the windows of the room. Perhaps you have seen a pier-glass in an $8 flat. A very thin and very agile person may, by observing his reflection in a rapid sequence of longitudinal strips, obtain a fairly accurate

appertaining: relating to
unassuming: humble, modest
sterling: of the highest quality
pier-glass: a type of mirror
agile: nimble; quick and graceful in movement
longitudinal: running lengthwise

conception of his looks. Della, being slender, had mastered the art.

Suddenly she whirled from the window and stood before the glass. Her eyes were shining brilliantly, but her face had lost its color within twenty seconds. Rapidly she pulled down her hair and let it fall to its full length.

Now, there were two possessions of the James Dillingham Youngs in which they both took a mighty pride. One was Jim's gold watch that had been his father's and his grandfather's. The other was Della's hair. Had the queen of Sheba lived in the flat across the airshaft, Della would have let her hair hang out the window some day to dry just to depreciate Her Majesty's jewels and gifts. Had King Solomon been the janitor, with all his treasures piled up in the basement, Jim would have pulled out his watch every time he passed, just to see him pluck at his beard from envy.

So now Della's beautiful hair fell about her rippling and shining like a cascade of brown waters. It reached below her knee and made itself almost a garment for her. And then she did it up again nervously and quickly. Once she faltered for a minute and stood still while a tear or two splashed on the worn red carpet.

On went her old brown jacket; on went her old brown hat. With a whirl of skirts and with the brilliant sparkle still in her eyes, she fluttered out the door and down the stairs to the street.

Where she stopped the sign read: "Mme. Sofronie. Hair Goods of All Kinds." One flight up Della ran, and collected herself, panting. Madame, large, too white, chilly, hardly looked the "Sofronie."

---

queen of Sheba: long-ago queen of an African kingdom, she is mentioned
   in the Bible, and also the subject of many legends
depreciate: to make less valuable
King Solomon: ruler of ancient Israel, known for his great wisdom

"Will you buy my hair?" asked Della.

"I buy hair," said Madame. "Take yer hat off and let's have a sight at the looks of it."

Down rippled the brown cascade.

"Twenty dollars," said Madame, lifting the mass with a practiced hand.

"Give it to me quick," said Della.

Oh, and the next two hours tripped by on rosy wings. Forget the hashed metaphor. She was ransacking the stores for Jim's present.

She found it at last. It surely had been made for Jim and no one else. There was no other like it in any of the stores, and she had turned all of them inside out. It was a platinum fob chain simple and chaste in design, properly proclaiming its value by substance alone and not by meretricious ornamentation—as all good things should do. It was even worthy of The Watch. As soon as she saw it she knew that it must be Jim's. It was like him. Quietness and value—the description applied to both. Twenty-one dollars they took from her for it, and she hurried home with the 87 cents. With that chain on his watch Jim might be properly anxious about the time in any company. Grand as the watch was, he sometimes looked at it on the sly on account of the old leather strap that he used in place of a chain.

When Della reached home her intoxication gave way a little to prudence and reason. She got out her curling irons and lighted the gas and went to work repairing the ravages made by

---

hashed: confused, mixed-up
ransacking: searching high and low
fob: a chain for a watch, or an ornament attached to such a chain
chaste: pure; simple in design
meretricious: gaudy; showy
intoxication: wild excitement
prudence: good judgment; common sense
ravages: destruction; great damage

generosity added to love. Which is always a tremendous task, dear friends—a mammoth task.

Within forty minutes her head was covered with tiny, close-lying curls that made her look wonderfully like a truant schoolboy. She looked at her reflection in the mirror long, carefully, and critically.

"If Jim doesn't kill me," she said to herself, "before he takes a second look at me, he'll say I look like a Coney Island chorus girl. But what could I do—oh! what could I do with a dollar and eighty-seven cents?"

At 7 o'clock the coffee was made and the frying-pan was on the back of the stove hot and ready to cook the chops.

Jim was never late. Della doubled the fob chain in her hand and sat on the corner of the table near the door that he always entered. Then she heard his step on the stair away down on the first flight, and she turned white for just a moment. She had a habit for saying a little silent prayer about the simplest everyday things, and now she whispered: "Please God, make him think I am still pretty."

The door opened and Jim stepped in and closed it. He looked thin and very serious. Poor fellow, he was only twenty-two—and to be burdened with a family! He needed a new overcoat and he was without gloves.

Jim stopped inside the door, as immovable as a setter at the scent of quail. His eyes were fixed upon Della, and there was an expression in them that she could not read, and it terrified her. It was not anger, nor surprise, nor disapproval, nor horror, nor any of the sentiments that she had been prepared for. He simply stared at her fixedly with that peculiar expression on his face.

truant: absent without permission
Coney Island: New York amusement park
setter: a type of long-haired hunting dog
quail: a type of small bird

Della wriggled off the table and went for him.

"Jim, darling," she cried, "don't look at me that way. I had my hair cut off and sold because I couldn't have lived through Christmas without giving you a present. It'll grow out again—you won't mind, will you? I just had to do it. My hair grows awfully fast. Say 'Merry Christmas!' Jim, and let's be happy. You don't know what a nice—what a beautiful, nice gift I've got for you."

"You've cut off your hair?" asked Jim, laboriously, as if he had not arrived at that patent fact yet even after the hardest mental labor.

"Cut it off and sold it," said Della. "Don't you like me just as well, anyhow? I'm me without my hair, ain't I?"

Jim looked about the room curiously.

"You say your hair is gone?" he said, with an air almost of idiocy.

"You needn't look for it," said Della. "It's sold, I tell you—sold and gone, too. It's Christmas Eve, boy. Be good to me, for it went for you. Maybe the hairs of my head were numbered," she went on with sudden serious sweetness, "but nobody could ever count my love for you. Shall I put the chops on, Jim?"

Out of his trance Jim seemed quickly to wake. He enfolded his Della. For ten seconds let us regard with discreet scrutiny some inconsequential object in the other direction. Eight dollars a week or a million a year—what is the difference? A mathematician or a wit would give you the wrong answer.

---

laboriously: with great effort
patent: obvious
discreet: quiet; not intruding
scrutiny: careful study; close inspection
inconsequential: unimportant

The magi brought valuable gifts, but that was not among them. This dark assertion will be illuminated later on.

Jim drew a package from his overcoat pocket and threw it upon the table.

"Don't make any mistake, Dell," he said, "about me. I don't think there's anything in the way of a haircut or a shave or a shampoo that could make me like my girl any less. But if you'll unwrap that package you may see why you had me going a while at first."

White fingers and nimble tore at the string and paper. And then an ecstatic scream of joy; and then, alas! a quick feminine change to hysterical tears and wails, necessitating the immediate employment of all the comforting powers of the lord of the flat.

For there lay The Combs—the set of combs, side and back, that Della had worshipped long in a Broadway window. Beautiful combs, pure tortoise shell, with jeweled rims—just the shade to wear in the beautiful vanished hair. They were expensive combs, she knew, and her heart had simply craved and yearned over them without the least hope of possession. And now, they were hers, but the tresses that should have adorned the coveted adornments were gone.

But she hugged them to her bosom, and at length she was able to look up with dim eyes and a smile and say: "My hair grows so fast, Jim!"

---

magi: in the Christian Bible, the three wise men who brought gifts to the baby Jesus
dark: unclear; difficult to understand; mysterious
assertion: a statement
illuminated: made clear (literally, have light shed on)
tresses: locks of hair
adorned: enhanced the appearance of; beautified
coveted: desired

And then Della leaped up like a little singed cat and cried, "Oh, oh!"

Jim had not yet seen his beautiful present. She held it out to him eagerly upon her open palm. The dull precious metal seemed to flash with a reflection of her bright and ardent spirit.

"Isn't it a dandy, Jim? I hunted all over town to find it. You'll have to look at the time a hundred times a day now. Give me your watch. I want to see how it looks on it."

Instead of obeying, Jim tumbled down on the couch and put his hands under the back of his head and smiled.

"Dell," said he, "let's put our Christmas presents away and keep 'em a while. They're too nice to use just at present. I sold the watch to get the money to buy your combs. And now suppose you put the chops on."

The magi, as you know, were wise men—wonderfully wise men—who brought gifts to the Babe in the manger. They invented the art of giving Christmas presents. Being wise, their gifts were no doubt wise ones, possibly bearing the privilege of exchange in case of duplication. And here I have lamely related to you the uneventful chronicle of two foolish children in a flat who most unwisely sacrificed for each other the greatest treasures of their house. But in a last word to the wise of these days let it be said that of all who give gifts these two were the wisest. Of all who give and receive gifts, such as they are wisest. Everywhere they are wisest. They are the magi.

---

ardent: full of strong emotion and warm feeling
lamely: weakly
chronicle: a story

# THE NECKLACE
*by Guy de Maupassant*

She was one of those pretty and charming young girls who
sometimes are born, as if by a mistake of destiny, into a
family of clerks. She had no dowry, no expectations, no way
of being known, understood, loved, married by any rich and
distinguished man; and so she let herself be married to a
little clerk of the Ministry of Education.

She dressed plainly because she could not dress well, but
she was as unhappy as if she had really fallen from her
proper place in life—since with women, there is neither caste
nor rank, because beauty, grace and charm take the place of
family and birth. Natural ingenuity, instinct for what is
elegant, and a supple mind are their sole hierarchy, and make
of women of the people the equals of the very greatest ladies.

Mathilde suffered ceaselessly, feeling herself born to enjoy
all delicacies and all luxuries. She was distressed at the
poverty of her dwelling, at the bareness of the walls, at the
shabby chairs, the ugliness of the curtains. All these things,
which another woman of her rank would never even have
noticed, tortured her and made her angry. The sight of the
little Breton peasant who did her humble housework aroused

---

dowry: money given by a bride's family to the groom at the time of
    their marriage
caste: social class based on rank and wealth
supple: capable of adapting quickly to new situations; flexible
sole: only
hierachy: a grouping or ranking into different levels, such as by wealth
    or social class
Breton: a native of Brittany, a region of France

in her despairing regrets and bewildering dreams. She thought of silent antechambers hung with Oriental tapestry, illumined by tall lamps of bronze, with two tall footmen in knee breeches asleep in the big armchairs, made drowsy by the oppressive heat of the stove. She thought of long reception halls hung with ancient silk, of the dainty cabinets containing priceless curiosities, and of the little coquettish perfumed reception rooms made for chatting at five o'clock with intimate friends, with men famous and sought after, whom all women envy and whose attention they all desire.

When she sat down to dinner, before the round table covered with a tablecloth used for three days, opposite her husband, who uncovered the soup tureen and declared with a delighted air, "Ah, the good soup! I don't know anything better than that," she thought of dainty dinners, of shining silverware, of tapestry that peopled the walls with ancient personages and with strange birds flying in the midst of a fairy forest; and she thought of delicious dishes served on marvelous plates and of the whispered gallantries to which you listen with a sphinx-like smile while you are eating the pink meat of a trout or the wings of a quail.

She had no gowns, no jewels, nothing. And she loved nothing but that. She felt made for that. She would have

---

bewildering: extremely confusing
antechambers: small rooms leading into larger rooms
tapestry: a heavy cloth, often with designs woven in, usually hung on walls
coquettish: having to do with flirting
intimate: close
tureen: a large bowl
gallantries: courteous and flattering words
sphinx-like: mysterious (like the Sphinx, the creature from Greek mythology noted for asking a challenging riddle)

liked so much to please, to be envied, to be charming, to be sought after.

She had a friend, a former schoolmate at the convent, who was rich, and whom she did not like to go to see any more because she felt so sad when she came home.

But one evening her husband came home with a triumphant air and holding a large envelope in his hand.

"There," said he, "there is something for you."

She tore the paper quickly and drew out a printed card which bore these words:

> *The Minister of Education and Madame Georges*
> *Ramponneau request the honor of M. and Mme. Loisel's*
> *company at the palace of the Ministry on Monday evening,*
> *January 18th.*

Instead of being delighted, as her husband had hoped, she threw the invitation on the table crossly, muttering, "What do you want me to do with that?"

"But, my dear, I thought you would be pleased. You never go out, and this is such a fine opportunity. I had great trouble to get it. Everyone wants to go; it is very select, and they are not giving many invitations to clerks. The whole official world will be there."

She looked at him with an irritated glance and said impatiently, "And what do you wish me to put on my back?"

He had not thought of that. He stammered, "Why, the gown you go to the theatre in. It looks very well to me."

He stopped, distracted, seeing that his wife was weeping. Two great tears ran slowly from the corners of her eyes toward the corners of her mouth.

---

M. and Mme.: Monsieur (Mister) and Madame (Mrs.)

"What's the matter? What's the matter?" he stuttered.

By a violent effort she conquered her grief and replied in a calm voice, while she wiped her wet cheeks, "Nothing. Only I have no gown, and, therefore I can't go to this ball. Give your card to some colleague whose wife is better equipped than I am."

He was in despair. He resumed, "See here, Mathilde. How much would it cost, a suitable gown, which you could use on other occasions—something very simple?"

She reflected several seconds, making her calculations and wondering also what sum she could ask without drawing on herself an immediate refusal and a frightened exclamation from the economical clerk.

Finally she replied, with hesitation, "I don't know exactly, but I think I could manage it with four hundred francs."

He grew a little pale, because he was setting aside just that amount to buy a gun and treat himself to a little shooting next summer on the plain of Nanterre, with several friends who went to shoot larks there on Sundays.

But he said, "Very well. I will give you four hundred francs. And try to have a pretty gown."

The day of the ball drew near and Madame Loisel seemed sad, restless, anxious. Her gown was ready, however.

Her husband said to her one evening, "What is the matter? Come, you have seemed very odd these last three days."

And she answered, "It annoys me not to have a single piece of jewelry, not a single ornament, nothing to put on. I shall look poverty-stricken. I would almost rather not go at all."

---

francs: French money

"You might wear natural flowers," said her husband. "They're very stylish at this time of year. For ten francs you can get two or three magnificent roses."

She was not convinced. "No; there's nothing more humiliating than to look poor among other women who are rich."

"How silly you are!" her husband cried. "Go look up your friend, Madame Forestier, and ask her to lend you some jewels. You know her quite well enough to do that."

She gave a cry of joy: "True! I never thought of it."

The next day she went to her friend and told her of her distress.

Madame Forestier went to a wardrobe with a mirror, took out a large jewel box, brought it back, opened it and said to Madame Loisel, "Choose, my dear."

She saw first some bracelets, then a pearl necklace, then a Venetian gold cross set with precious stones, of admirable workmanship. She tried on the ornaments before the mirror, hesitated, and could not make up her mind to part with them, to give them back. She kept asking, "Haven't you any more?"

"Why, yes. Look further; I don't know what you like."

Suddenly she discovered, in a black satin box, a superb diamond necklace, and her heart throbbed with an immoderate desire. Her hands trembled as she took it. She fastened it round her throat, outside her high-necked waist, and was lost in ecstasy at her reflection in the mirror.

Then she asked, hesitating, filled with anxious doubt, "Will you lend me this, only this?"

---

humiliating: humbling; extremely embarrassing
immoderate: excessive; extreme

"Why, yes, certainly."

She threw her arms round her friend's neck, kissed her with great emotion, then fled with her treasure.

The night of the ball arrived. Madame Loisel was a great success. She was prettier than any other woman there, elegant, graceful, smiling, and wild with joy. All the men looked at her, asked her name, sought to be introduced. All the officials of the Cabinet wished to waltz with her. She was noticed by the minister himself.

She danced with rapture, with passion, intoxicated by pleasure, forgetting all in the triumph of her beauty, in the glory of her success, in a sort of cloud of happiness made up of all this admiration, of all these awakened desires, and of this victory so complete and so sweet to a woman's heart.

She left the ball about four o'clock in the morning. Her husband had been sleeping since midnight in a little deserted anteroom with three other gentlemen whose wives were enjoying the ball.

He threw over her shoulders the wraps he had brought, the modest wraps of common life, the poverty of which contrasted with the elegance of the ball dress. She felt this and wished to escape so as not to be noticed by the other women, who were enveloping themselves in costly furs.

Loisel held her back, saying, "Wait a bit. You will catch cold outside. I will call a cab."

But she did not listen to him and rapidly descended the stairs. When they reached the street, they could not find a

---

rapture: ecstasy; great happiness
intoxicated: wildly excited
anteroom: a waiting room

carriage and began to look for one, shouting after the cabmen passing at a distance.

They went toward the Seine in despair, shivering with cold. At last they found on the quay one of those ancient night cabs which, as though they were ashamed to show their shabbiness during the day, are never seen round Paris until after dark.

It took them to their dwelling in the Rue des Martyrs, and sadly they mounted the stairs to their flat. All was ended for her. As to him, he reflected that he must be at the ministry at ten o'clock that morning.

She removed her wraps before the glass so as to see herself once more in all her glory. But suddenly she uttered a cry. She no longer had the necklace around her neck!

"What is the matter with you?" demanded her husband, already half undressed.

She turned distractedly toward him. "I have—I have—I've lost Madame Forestier's necklace," she cried.

He stood up, bewildered. "What!—how? Impossible!"

They looked among the folds of her skirt, of her cloak, in her pockets, everywhere, but did not find it.

"You're sure you had it on when you left the ball?" he asked.

"Yes, I felt it in the vestibule of the palace."

"But if you had lost it in the street we should have heard it fall. It must be in the cab."

"Yes, probably. Did you take his number?"

"No. And you—didn't you notice it?"

"No."

They looked at each other, thunderstruck. At last Loisel put on his clothes.

---

quay: a riverside area where ships may dock
thunderstruck: shocked, amazed

"I shall go back on foot," said he, "over the whole route, to see whether I can find it."

He went out. She sat waiting on a chair in her ball dress, without strength to go to bed, overwhelmed, without any fire, without a thought.

Her husband returned about seven o'clock. He had found nothing.

He went to police headquarters, to the newspaper offices to offer a reward; he went to the cab companies—everywhere he was urged by the least spark of hope.

She waited all day, in the same condition of mad fear before this terrible calamity.

Loisel returned at night with a hollow, pale face. He had discovered nothing.

"You must write to your friend," said he, "that you have broken the clasp of her necklace and that you are having it mended. That will give us time to turn round."

She wrote as he dictated.

At the end of a week they had lost all hope. Loisel, who had aged five years, declared, "We must consider how to replace those jewels."

The next day they took the case and went to the jeweler whose name was in the cover. He consulted his books.

"It was not I, madame, who sold that necklace; I must simply have furnished the case."

Then they went from jeweler to jeweler, searching for a necklace like the other, trying to recall it, both sick with grief and anxiety.

They found, in a shop at the Palais Royal, a string of diamonds that seemed to them exactly like the one they had lost. It was worth forty thousand francs. They could have it for thirty-six.

So they begged the jeweler not to sell it for three days yet. And they made a bargain that he should buy it back for thirty-four thousand francs, in case they should find the lost necklace before the end of February.

Loisel possessed eighteen thousand francs that his father had left him. He would borrow the rest.

He did borrow, asking a thousand francs of one, five hundred of another, five louis here, three louis there. He gave notes, took up ruinous obligations, dealt with usurers and all manner of lenders. He compromised all the rest of his life, risked signing a note without even knowing whether he could meet it; and, frightened by the trouble yet to come, by the black misery that was about to fall upon him, by the prospect of all the physical privations and moral tortures that he was to suffer, he went to get the new necklace, laying upon the jeweler's counter thirty-six thousand francs.

When Madame Loisel took back the necklace Madame Forestier said to her with a chilly manner, "You should have returned it sooner; I might have needed it."

She did not open the case, as her friend had so much feared. If she had detected the substitution, what would she have thought, what would she have said? Would she not have taken Madame Loisel for a thief?

---

louis: French money
usurers: those who lend money at excessive interest rates

Thereafter Madame Loisel knew the horrible existence of the needy. She bore her part, however, with sudden heroism. That dreadful debt must be paid. She would pay it. They dismissed their servant; they changed their lodgings; they rented a garret under the roof.

She came to know what heavy housework meant and the odious cares of the kitchen. She washed the dishes, using her dainty fingers and rosy nails on greasy pots and pans. She washed the soiled linen, the shirts and the dishcloths, which she dried upon a line; she carried the garbage down to the street every morning and carried up the water, stopping for breath at every landing. And, dressed like a woman of the people, she went to the fruit seller, the grocer, the butcher, a basket on her arm, bargaining, meeting with insults, defending her miserable money, sou by sou.

Every month they had to pay off some notes, renew others, obtain more time.

Her husband worked evenings, keeping a tradesman's accounts, and late at night he often copied manuscript for five sous a page.

This life lasted ten years.

At the end of ten years they had paid everything, everything, with the rates of usury and the accumulations of the compound interest.

Madame Loisel looked old now. She had become the woman of impoverished households—strong and hard and rough. With frowsy hair, skirts askew, and red hands, she talked loud while washing the floor with great swishes of water. But sometimes, when her husband was at the office,

---

odious: hateful; terrible
impoverished: made poor; reduced to poverty

she sat down near the window and she thought of that happy evening long ago, of that ball where she had been so beautiful and so admired.

What would have happened if she had not lost that necklace? Who knows? Who knows? How strange and changeful is life! How small a thing is needed to make or ruin us!

But one Sunday, having gone to take a walk in the Champs Elysees to refresh herself after the labors of the week, she suddenly perceived a woman who was leading a child. It was Madame Forestier, still young, still beautiful, still charming.

Madame Loisel felt moved. Should she speak to her? Yes, certainly. And now that she had paid, she would tell her all about it. Why not?

She went up.

"Good-day, Jeanne."

The other, astonished to be greeted familiarly by this woman of the people, did not recognize her at all and stammered, "But—madame!—I do not know—You must be mistaken."

"No. I am Mathilde Loisel."

Her friend uttered a cry. "Oh, my poor Mathilde! How you are changed!"

"Yes, I have had a hard life since I last saw you, and great poverty—and that because of you!"

"Of me! How so?"

"Do you remember that diamond necklace you lent me to wear at the ministerial ball?"

"Yes. Well?"

"Well, I lost it."

"What do you mean? You brought it back."

"I brought you back another exactly like it. And it has taken us ten years to pay for it. You can understand that it was not easy for us, for us who had nothing. At last it is ended, and I am very glad."

Madame Forestier had stopped.

"You say that you bought a necklace of diamonds to replace mine?"

"Yes. You never noticed it, then! They were very similar."

And she smiled with proud and naive joy.

Madame Forestier, deeply moved, took her hands.

"Oh, my poor Mathilde! Why, my necklace was paste! It was worth at most only five hundred francs!"

---

naive: simple; lacking sophistication

paste: a shiny kind of glass used to make artificial gems

# THE NECKLACE
*by Guy de Maupassant*
*adapted by Earl J. Dias*

*Characters*

**CECILE FORESTIER**

**MATHILDE LOISEL**

**CHARLES LOISEL,** *Mathilde's husband*

**MADAME GROUET,** *a peddler*

**RENAULT,** *a peddler*

**LISETTE,** *15*

## SCENE 1

*Time:* A JANUARY EVENING IN THE LATE 19TH CENTURY.
*Setting:* THE LOISEL APARTMENT IN PARIS. *The shabbily furnished room includes a worn armchair. Table at center is set for two, with a large soup bowl at each place, and a loaf of French bread in center of table. Exit left leads outside.*
*At Rise: Mathilde Loisel sits at table, and Cecile Forestier sits in armchair.*

**CECILE:** To think, Mathilde, that I have seen you only twice since our school days. That is why I took the liberty of dropping by today.

**MATHILDE:** I'm glad you did, Cecile. It is pleasant to see you. *(Looking around room)* But you can see why I do not invite any of my old school friends here. This is scarcely a palace, and certainly not the kind of luxury you are accustomed to.

**CECILE:** You deserve better, Mathilde—a woman as beautiful as you. *(She smiles.)* Do you remember how you used to dream?

**MATHILDE** *(Bitterly):* I remember. I used to hope that some day I would live in a huge mansion. I'd have vestibules hung with Oriental tapestries and lighted by tall lamps of bronze. *(Laughing wryly)* I was to have large parlors decked with old silk, and, oh, yes, little rooms, prepared and perfumed for a five o'clock chit-chat with intimate friends. *(Shrugs)* So, here I am.

**CECILE:** And your husband, Charles. How is he?

**MATHILDE:** Charles means well. He is good-hearted and does his best, but the salary of a minor clerk in the Ministry of Education is not much.

**CECILE:** You could have done better. Do you remember how the Marquis de Montclair was taken with you? He used to send you flowers, and…

**MATHILDE** *(Dreamily):* Ah, the Marquis. He was so elegant, so charming. (She sighs in resignation.) But he was not for me—a poor girl with no dowry to offer. My parents did the best they could for me by arranging my marriage to Charles.

**CECILE:** And a lucky man he is to have won himself such a beauty.

**MATHILDE:** Beauty? *(Gestures around room)* What good is it in these surroundings? All my life I have dreamed of dining

scarcely: hardly
resignation: sad acceptance

in famous restaurants—Maxim's, Fouquet's—of dancing among the rich, but you see where I am. What have I to look forward to?

CECILE *(Rising and coming to her):* My poor Mathilde.

MATHILDE: The least I can do is to offer you a cup of tea.

CECILE: No. Thank you, but I must be on my way. Marcel and I are dining tonight with the Count de Guiche.

MATHILDE: How I envy you! *(Bitterly)* Charles and I are dining here as you can see. *(Charles Loisel enters, with newspaper under his arm.)*

CHARLES: Good evening, Mathilde. *(Surprised)* Why, Madame Forestier! I have not seen you in many months.

CECILE *(Shaking Charles's hand):* How nice to see you, Monsieur Loisel.

CHARLES: I am glad you paid us a visit. Mathilde is alone a good deal. Will you stay to eat with us?

MATHILDE *(Quickly):* Cecile has a dinner engagement, Charles. *(Rises)*

CHARLES: That is too bad. Perhaps another time.

CECILE *(Kindly):* Of course, another time. But now I must go. We must see each other soon, Mathilde. There is no reason for us to be strangers.

MATHILDE *(Accompanying her to door):* Yes, we will meet again soon. *(Mathilde and Cecile exit. Charles sits at table, tucks napkin under his chin, unfolds newspaper, and begins to read. After a moment, Mathilde reenters.)*

CHARLES: Madame Forestier looks most prosperous.

MATHILDE: As well she should. Her husband has one of the great fortunes in France.

CHARLES: Lucky fellow.

MATHILDE: Lucky woman.

CHARLES: I am devilishly hungry tonight. This winter air gives a man an appetite.

MATHILDE *(Dully)*: I'll get the dinner. *(Charles continues to read the newspaper. Mathilde exits and then returns with a tureen of soup. She ladles soup into Charles's bowl. Charles puts newspaper aside.)*

CHARLES *(Breaking off piece of bread from loaf and sniffing his soup)*: Ah, such good soup!

MATHILDE *(Ladling soup into her own bowl; ironically)*: Ah, yes, such good soup. *(She places tureen on table and sits. Charles eats eagerly, dipping his bread into bowl. Mathilde, watching him with distaste, eats more delicately.)*

CHARLES: This soup is as good as my mother used to make! *(Mops his bowl with bread)*

MATHILDE: Would you like more?

CHARLES: All in good time, but first I have a surprise for you.

MATHILDE *(Taken aback)*: A surprise?

CHARLES: Something that should please you very much. *(He takes envelope from his pocket, opens it and draws out a card.)* Listen. *(Reading; importantly)* "The Minister of Education and Madame Georges Ramponeau request the honor of M. and Mme. Loisel's presence at the Palace of the Ministry on Monday, January 18." *(Proudly)* Now, what do you think of that, Mathilde?

MATHILDE *(Sharply)*: What do you expect me to think of that?

CHARLES *(Bewildered)*: But, my dear, I thought you would be pleased. You never go out, and here's a chance—a fine one. These invitations are greatly sought after, and not many are given to the clerks. Everyone in the official world will be at this party.

MATHILDE *(Impatiently)*: What do you expect me to wear?

CHARLES: Why, the dress in which you go to the theater. That looks very pretty to me. (*Mathilde puts her face in her hands and begins to sob. Charles, in surprise*) What is the matter, Mathilde? Why are you crying?

MATHILDE (*Controlling herself; wiping tears from her cheek*): I have no clothes to wear to this party. Give your invitation to some colleague whose wife has a more suitable gown than I. (*Charles looks hurt. He frowns, deep in thought.*)

CHARLES: See here, Mathilde—how much would a simple dress cost? Something that would do on other occasions, too?

MATHILDE (*Hesitating*): I—I don't know, exactly. (*Frowns*) But it seems to me that four hundred francs might do.

CHARLES (*Alarmed*): Four hundred francs! (*Shakes his head, then continues quickly*) Still, we might do it. I had been saving for a gun. I thought I might do some shooting at Nanterre next summer, but this is more important. (*Firmly*) Yes, you shall have the four hundred francs. (*Forcing a smile*) But take care to buy a pretty dress.

MATHILDE: Oh, Charles! (*She jumps up, comes to Charles, and kisses him on the cheek.*) How generous you are! And I assure you it will be a pretty dress. (*She frowns suddenly.*) But no, it is really impossible.

CHARLES: Impossible? Why?

MATHILDE: The women at the Ministry will not only be beautifully dressed but will wear handsome jewels as well. (*She returns to her place at the table.*) It annoys me not to have a jewel, not a single one. I shall look plain and homely.

CHARLES: You can wear some natural flowers. They are very stylish this time of year. For ten francs, you can get two or three magnificent roses.

MATHILDE *(Shaking her head):* No, there's nothing more humiliating than to look poor among a lot of rich women.

CHARLES: But, Mathilde, I'm afraid I cannot help you there. The dress, yes, but jewelry is beyond our reach.

MATHILDE: That is just what I have been telling you. *(Charles stares moodily at his plate. Mathilde toys with a piece of bread. Suddenly, Charles bangs the table.)*

CHARLES: I have it! Why did I not think of it before? Your friend, Madame Forestier.

MATHILDE: What about her?

CHARLES: Ask her to lend you some jewelry. She has so much. Why, she was wearing a ring with a diamond as big as an onion. She likes you. I am sure she would let you borrow some bauble or other.

MATHILDE *(Musing):* That's true. I had not thought of it. *(More cheerfully)* What a wonderful idea, Charles! *(Rising)* I shall go to her house at once. I'm sure I can catch her before she leaves for dinner at the Count's.

CHARLES *(Relieved):* Good! I'll clean up here while you're gone.

MATHILDE *(Happily):* It will be a splendid party, will it not, Charles?

CHARLES: You will be the most beautiful woman there.

MATHILDE: I hope so. But now I must get dressed and run. *(She exits hurriedly. Charles rises, sighs, shrugs, and begins to clear dishes from table. Curtain)*

---

bauble: a small ornament, such as a piece of jewelry, of little value

## SCENE 2

*Time:* A FEW DAYS LATER; THE DAY OF THE PARTY.

*Setting:* SAME AS SCENE 1.

*At Rise: Charles, wearing a suit, sits at table. He draws his watch from his pocket, looks at it, and shakes his head.*

**CHARLES** *(Loudly):* Mathilde! Are you ready? We should be there by eight.

**MATHILDE** *(Offstage):* Coming, Charles. *(After a moment or two Mathilde, wearing a lovely gown, appears in doorway and poses for a moment. She holds a necklace.)* How do I look?

**CHARLES** *(Rising and gazing at her admiringly):* You are more beautiful than ever, Mathilde.

**MATHILDE:** Now you shall see what I borrowed from Cecile. I did not show it to you before because I wished to surprise you. *(She displays the necklace.)* Look. Is it not lovely?

**CHARLES:** It is magnificent!

**MATHILDE:** Help me clasp it around my neck. *(Charles does so.)*

**CHARLES** *(Standing off to look at her):* Perfect!

**MATHILDE** *(Posing happily):* You see, it is simple but expensive looking. Oh, I thought for a long time before I chose it, Charles. Cecile has such a collection of jewelry; I was tempted by all of it. Bracelets, a pearl necklace, a Venetian brooch set with precious stones. I tried on all of them and posed before the glass. And then I discovered in a box lined with satin this superb necklace of diamonds. I was in ecstasy when I put it on.

**CHARLES:** It was a wise choice, my dear.

---

brooch: a pin worn as jewelry, usually near the neck

163

MATHILDE: And now I shall get my wrap, and I will be ready. *(Happily doing a little pirouette)* Oh, Charles, it will be a wonderful evening—one of the great nights of our lives. *(They exit. Lights dim briefly to denote the passage of time.)*

## SCENE 3

*Time:* A FEW HOURS LATER.
*Setting:* SAME AS SCENE 2
*At Rise: Charles and Mathilde enter.*

MATHILDE *(Gleefully):* What a glorious party!
CHARLES *(Sinking wearily into chair):* You certainly were a success, Mathilde. *(Wryly)* After midnight, I just retired to the anteroom with three other men whose wives were also having a good time.
MATHILDE: I danced with everyone—all the most distinguished men! The Count de Brisaille, the Marquis Saint-Challet, Monsieur Deveau—even the Minister himself.
CHARLES: So I observed. All the men were looking at you, inquiring your name, and asking to be introduced.
MATHILDE *(Dancing gracefully around the room):* I shall never be able to sleep tonight. I am on a cloud of happiness.
CHARLES *(Yawning):* As for me, I shall sleep like a log. Night life is too much for me.
MATHILDE: Charles, how can you say that? Tonight was life as it should be—glittering, romantic, joyful. *(Removes her wrap, throws it onto table, continues to dance)*

---

pirouette: a rapid full turn
denote: indicate

**CHARLES** *(Stifling another yawn):* Aren't you too tired to dance, my dear? *(Mathilde laughs, twirls about, then stops suddenly, her hand at her neck. She utters startled cry.)*

**CHARLES** *(Alarmed):* What is it?

**MATHILDE** *(Terrified):* The necklace! It's gone!

**CHARLES** *(Jumping up):* It must be here somewhere. *(Picks up wrap)* Perhaps in the folds of your wrap. *(He searches frantically.)* It's not here!

**MATHILDE** *(Disturbed):* Look in your coat pocket, Charles. Perhaps I gave it to you.

CHARLES: No, I am sure you did not. But let us see. (*Turns his pockets inside out.*) No, not there. (*He goes toward door.*) Perhaps you dropped it on the stairs. I shall look. (*He exits hurriedly. Mathilde begins to look frantically around room— under table and chairs—then looks again in folds of her wrap. In distress*) Oh, where could it be? (*After a moment, Charles reenters.*)

MATHILDE (*Hopefully*): Did you find it?

CHARLES (*Shaking head*): Not a trace. It is not on the stairs. And I was lucky because the cab we came in is still outside. The driver is feeding his horse. The necklace is not in the cab.

MATHILDE (*Miserably*): What are we to do?

CHARLES: Are you sure you had it when we left the party?

MATHILDE: Yes. I touched it in the vestibule of the Ministry.

CHARLES: Perhaps it will turn up, but I fear we are out of luck, Mathilde. The chances are you dropped it on the street. And the streets of Paris being what they are, I doubt if anyone who finds so valuable a necklace will even report it to the police.

MATHILDE (*Bitterly*): Why did this have to happen? Does fate begrudge us one night of pleasure?

CHARLES (*Sharply*): I do not know about fate, Mathilde. But I know that we must do something about this. First of all, you must write to Madame Forestier. Tell her that you have broken the clasp of her necklace and are having it repaired. That will give us more time to search for it.

MATHILDE (*Eagerly*): Yes, I will do that at once. (*She exits quickly and returns in a moment with paper, pen, and ink, which she places on table.*)

---

begrudge: to envy what someone else has; to give but only with great reluctance

**CHARLES:** If the necklace does not turn up, we must, of course, replace it.

**MATHILDE** *(Incredulously):* Replace it? But, Charles, the necklace must be worth a fortune!

**CHARLES:** I know it is worth a fortune. There is a jeweler's shop in the Palais Royal not far from the Ministry. I pass it every day. There is a necklace in the window that is almost an exact replica of Madame Forestier's.

**MATHILDE** *(Eagerly):* And the cost?

**CHARLES** *(Grimly):* Forty thousand francs.

**MATHILDE** *(In dismay):* Forty thousand francs! We could not afford it in a lifetime!

**CHARLES:** If the other is not found, we must afford it. After all, Mathilde, I may not have much money, but I pride myself on being an honest man.

**MATHILDE:** But forty thousand francs!

**CHARLES:** I have, as you know, eighteen thousand francs which my father left me. I have never touched it. That can be a start.

**MATHILDE:** And the rest?

**CHARLES:** We must borrow it.

**MATHILDE:** But, Charles, we shall then be in the hands of the moneylenders. You remember what happened when Monsieur LeBreque's business failed. He borrowed, asking a thousand francs here, five hundred there, a few louis elsewhere. He gave promissory notes, dealt with usurers. When he died, he was living in poverty, and the debt was still unpaid.

**CHARLES** *(Miserably):* I know. But what would you have us do? Do you want to go to Madame Forestier and say, "I'm

---

promissory notes: "I.O.U.'s"

sorry, Cecile, but a little accident happened. I lost your forty-thousand-franc necklace. Ha! Ha! These things will happen, won't they?"

MATHILDE *(Tearfully):* You are being cruel, Charles.

CHARLES: Not cruel, Mathilde—honest. One has to face the troubles that come in life. *(More gently)* Come now, Mathilde. Write that note to Madame Forestier. I will post it before I go to bed. *(Mathilde picks up her pen, thinks for a moment, and then begins to write. Charles sits staring thoughtfully into space. Suddenly, Mathilde stops writing, puts her head down on table, and begins to sob. Charles rises and goes to her, putting his hand on her shoulder.)*

CHARLES: There! There! We will meet this together. *(She continues to sob. He pats her shoulder and shakes his head.)* What a little thing it takes to save you or to ruin you. *(Curtain)*

## SCENE 4

*Time:* TEN YEARS LATER.

*Setting:* THE LOISELS' ATTIC ROOM, IN THE PARIS SLUMS. *The only furniture is a battered old table and three or four rickety wooden chairs.*

*At Rise: Mathilde, mop in hand, a bucket of water by her side, is washing the floor. She looks older, and there are traces of gray in her hair. Her sleeves are rolled to her elbows, and she wears a dirty apron. Children's voices are heard shouting outside. Mathilde, irritated, goes to window, and calls out.*

MATHILDE: Shut your mouths down there, you street rats! You get noisier every day! Can't one get at least a little peace and quiet in this miserable neighborhood? Go home to your mothers—if you have any! (*Children's voices die away. Mathilde returns to center and resumes mopping.*) Noisy brats! (*Charles enters. He looks tired, seedy, and much older. He is carrying a ledger.*)

CHARLES (*Yawning*): I was up all night with these accounts. I tell you, Mathilde, to work all day at my own job and then to do accounts on the side for the little money they bring in is almost too much.

MATHILDE (*Harshly*): You should be used to it by now. We've had ten years of this miserable life.

CHARLES: At least our debts are finally paid.

MATHILDE: Oh, yes, our debts are paid. (*Bitterly*) And look at me. Is this the Mathilde you married?

CHARLES (*Wearily*): We have both changed. Time changes us all. (*Sighing*) Well, I must be off to the Ministry. I'll be lucky if I can keep my eyes open. (*He exits.*)

MADAME GROUET (*Offstage*): Vegetables! Vegetables for sale!

MATHILDE (*Going to window and speaking coarsely*): Come up! Let us see what garbage you are peddling this morning! (*After a moment, Madame Grouet enters. She carries a basket of cabbages and carrots.*)

MADAME GROUET: Bonjour, Madame Loisel. I have some lovely vegetables today.

MATHILDE: You've been saying that for ten years, Madame Grouet, and your vegetables get worse each year. (*Taking a cabbage from basket and feeling it*) Ugh! This cabbage is old enough to be your grandmother.

MADAME GROUET: But, madame, I swear it was picked fresh this morning.

---

Bonjour: a French greeting, meaning "Good day," "Good morning," or
"Good afternoon"

MATHILDE (*Fingering carrots*): And these carrots are loaded with worms.

MADAME GROUET: But no, madame—they are jewels of carrots.

MATHILDE: How much for this grandmother cabbage?

MADAME GROUET: Twenty sous.

MATHILDE (*Throwing cabbage back into basket*): Take your basket and sell your wares to the other fools in the neighborhood, you old fraud. Twenty sous! Why, you old robber, it is not worth ten.

MADAME GROUET: Please, madame, at twenty sous it is an immense bargain.

MATHILDE (*Turning her back on Madame Grouet*): Do you think I'm a lunatic?

MADAME GROUET: Madame is unkind. (*Slyly*) But I will offer you a real bargain. You may have the cabbage for fifteen sous. (*Mathilde resumes mopping, pushing mop at Madame Grouet's feet.*)

MATHILDE: Be off with you!

MADAME GROUET (*Trying to avoid the mop*): But it is a real bargain.

MATHILDE (*Stopping her work and leaning on mop*): I'll give you twelve sous. No more.

MADAME GROUET: Ah, madame drives a hard bargain. But one must live. It is yours, madame, for twelve sous.

MATHILDE: And robbery at that. (*Mathilde puts the cabbage on table, then takes a worn purse from her apron pocket and counts out twelve coins, one by one, into Madame Grouet's hand.*)

MADAME GROUET: Ah, thank you, madame. You will find that cabbage to be the king of all cabbages. Delicious!

MATHILDE: Save the speeches for the other poor fools you

deal with. Now go. I'm busy. *(Madame Grouet exits quickly, as Mathilde resumes mopping furiously. Grumbling as she works)* Ah, what a miserable life! I work all day and eat rotten vegetables at night!

**RENAULT** *(Offstage):* Beef! Veal! Freshly killed chickens! *(Mathilde stops mopping, smiles grimly, exits, and returns with a paper bag, which she places on table. Then she goes right and calls.)*

**MATHILDE:** Monsieur Renault! Come up!

**RENAULT:** Oui, madame! At once! *(Renault enters, wearing a stained butcher's apron and carrying a basket.)*

**RENAULT:** Bonjour, Madame Loisel. I have here a special piece of veal for you. Young, tender—the dew is still on it.

**MATHILDE** *(Taking paper bag from table and shaking it in his face):* Listen, you old goat. I have here a piece of beef you sold me yesterday.

**RENAULT:** Yes, I remember. A magnificent cut. Fit for a king.

**MATHILDE** *(Throwing the bag at him):* It's as tough as rope. I cooked it all day, and we still couldn't eat it. And for this gristle, you charged me fifty sous, you old crook!

**RENAULT** *(Picking up bag):* But, madame, there must be some mistake.

**MATHILDE:** There is—and you made it! I want my fifty sous back!

**RENAULT:** But that is not good business, madame. I sold you the meat in good faith.

**MATHILDE** *(Advancing with the mop and shaking it at him):* I want my fifty sous!

**RENAULT** *(Retreating and speaking coaxingly):* But, madame, that is not business. *(She again shakes the mop at him.)* Be reasonable. I will give you this piece of tender veal in

oui: French for "yes"

exchange for the beef. This will prove I am an honest man.

MATHILDE *(Angrily)*: You don't have an honest bone in your body! I want my fifty sous back.

RENAULT: Very well, madame. *(He reaches into his pocket and hands her coins, which she counts carefully.)*

MATHILDE *(Looking up)*: You robber! There are only forty-eight sous here!

RENAULT: Forty-eight? *(He looks carefully at coins in Mathilde's hand.)* But, of course. I made a mistake in counting. *(He gives Mathilde two sous more.)* There. Again I prove I am an honest man.

MATHILDE: Ha! That's the best joke I've heard today.

RENAULT: But now about this veal, madame. You have my word for it—it is an exquisite cut. From a prize calf, no less. *(He takes bag from his basket, holds it up.)* And at the unbelievably low price of fifty-five sous. Reduced from sixty, just for you, madame.

MATHILDE: That veal would probably break whatever teeth I have left.

RENAULT: But, madame, I swear on my honor—

MATHILDE *(Advancing on him and shaking the mop at him)*: Get out! I've had enough of your tricks for one day!

RENAULT *(Retreating)*: But the veal—

MATHILDE: This is for the veal! *(She takes a vicious swipe at him with the mop, and he exits hurriedly. Mathilde goes to table, sits, and counts the fifty sous again. She begins to laugh robustly. Lisette, a girl of 15, enters.)*

LISETTE: You seem happy, Madame Loisel.

MATHILDE: When one outwits a thief, one has a right to be

happy. What do you want, Lisette?

**LISETTE:** There is a woman out there who has been asking for you.

**MATHILDE:** What does she look like?

**LISETTE:** She is very pretty, and she is wearing the loveliest dress.

**MATHILDE:** Well, tell her to come up. Anyone dressed well will be a welcome change in this neighborhood of scarecrows.

**LISETTE** *(Meekly):* Yes, madame. *(She goes to door.)* I'll tell the lady she may come up. *(Exits. Mathilde resumes mopping. After a moment, Cecile Forestier enters.).*

**CECILE:** Oh, I am sorry. There must be some mistake. I was looking for Madame Loisel. *(Mathilde looks up, is surprised, and smiles.)*

**MATHILDE:** Good morning, Cecile.

**CECILE:** But, madame, I do not know you. Are you not making a mistake? *(Mathilde goes to her, takes her hand, and leads her to center.)*

**MATHILDE:** There is no mistake, Cecile. I am Mathilde Loisel.

**CECILE** *(Gazing closely at her and uttering a startled cry):* Oh! My poor Mathilde! How you have changed!

**MATHILDE:** Yes, I have had hard days since I last saw you. And many troubles—all because of you.

**CECILE** *(Stunned):* Because of me? How so? It has been at least ten years since I have seen you.

**MATHILDE:** You remember the diamond necklace that you lent me to wear to the ball at the Ministry?

**CECILE:** Yes. What of it?

MATHILDE: Well, I lost it.

CECILE: But how can that be? You brought it back to me soon after the ball.

MATHILDE: I brought you back another just like it—one that cost forty thousand francs. And now for ten years Charles and I have been paying for it. You must understand that it was not easy for us who have nothing. But, at last our debt is paid, and I am very glad. *(Long pause)*

CECILE *(With difficulty):* You—you say that you bought a diamond necklace to replace mine?

MATHILDE *(Smiling proudly):* Yes. You did not even notice it, did you? They were exactly alike! *(Cecile looks desolate and sadly shakes her head. Much moved, she takes both of Mathilde's hands. Mathilde looks questioningly at her.)* Cecile, what is it?

CECILE: Oh, my poor Mathilde! *(She pauses.)* The necklace that I lent you was only a paste imitation—they were not real diamonds! *(Mathilde looks horrified.)* At most, it was worth five hundred francs. *(Mathilde, stunned, sways as though about to faint as Cecile grasps her. Quick curtain)*

---

desolate: joyless; sorrowful; hopeless

# FAVORITES FROM FAMOUS BOOKS

# *A CHRISTMAS CAROL*

# A CHRISTMAS CAROL
### by Charles Dickens

*A Christmas Carol was originally written in about fifty thousand words, but when Charles Dickens began a series of public readings in America, he condensed the tale to about a quarter of its original length, in order to bring it within the limits of an evening's entertainment. The following version is based in part on the form of the story Dickens used in his public readings.*

### STAVE I: MARLEY'S GHOST

Marley was dead, to begin with. There is no doubt whatever about that. The register of his burial was signed by the clergyman, the clerk, the undertaker, and the chief mourner. Scrooge signed it. And Scrooge's name was good upon 'Change for anything he chose to put his hand to.

Old Marley was as dead as a door-nail.

Scrooge knew he was dead? Of course he did. How could it be otherwise? Scrooge and he were partners for I don't know how many years. Scrooge was his sole executor, his sole administrator, his sole assign, his sole residuary legatee,

---

stave: a stanza in music (as part of this "carol")
register: written public record
'Change: the Royal Exchange, where bankers, merchants, and others met to do business
sole: only
executor: someone who carries out a person's will when that person dies (*administrator, assign,* and *residuary legatee* are also legal terms having to do with a will)

his sole friend, and sole mourner. And even Scrooge was not so dreadfully cut up by the sad event, but that he was an excellent man of business on the very day of the funeral, and solemnized it with an undoubted bargain.

The mention of Marley's funeral brings me back to the point I started from. There is no doubt that Marley was dead. This must be distinctly understood, or nothing wonderful can come of the story I am going to relate.

Scrooge never painted out Old Marley's name. There it stood, years afterwards, above the warehouse door: *Scrooge and Marley.*

Oh! But he was a tight-fisted hand at the grindstone, Scrooge! a squeezing, wrenching, grasping, scraping, clutching, covetous old sinner! Hard and sharp as flint, from which no steel had ever struck out generous fire; secret, and self-contained, and solitary as an oyster. The cold within him froze his old features, nipped his pointed nose, shriveled his cheek, stiffened his gait; made his eyes red, his thin lips blue; and spoke out shrewdly in his grating voice. A frosty rime was on his head, and on his eyebrows, and his wiry chin. He carried his own low temperature always about with him; he iced his office in the dog days, and didn't thaw it one degree at Christmas.

---

cut up: slang expression for "upset, disturbed"
solemnized: marked the occasion with seriousness or in a
   religious manner
covetous: extremely greedy
gait: manner of walking
rime: a hard, frosty crust
dog days: the hottest days in the year

Nobody ever stopped him in the street to say, with gladsome looks, "My dear Scrooge, how are you? When will you come to see me?" No beggars implored him to bestow a trifle, no children asked him what it was o'clock, no man or woman ever once in all his life inquired the way to such and such a place, of Scrooge. Even the blind men's dogs appeared to know him; and when they saw him coming on, would tug their owners into doorways and up courts; and then would wag their tails as though they said, "No eye at all is better than an evil eye, dark master!"

Once upon a time—of all the good days in the year, on Christmas Eve—old Scrooge sat busy in his countinghouse. It was cold, bleak, biting weather, foggy withal, and he could hear the people in the court outside go wheezing up and down, beating their hands upon their breasts, and stamping their feet upon the pavement stones to warm them. The city clocks had only just gone three, but it was quite dark already—it had not been light all day—and candles were flaring in the windows of the neighboring offices, like ruddy smears upon the palpable brown air. The fog came pouring in at every chink and keyhole, and was so dense without, that although the court was of the narrowest, the houses opposite were mere phantoms.

The door of Scrooge's countinghouse was open that he might keep his eye upon his clerk, who in a dismal little cell beyond, a sort of tank, was copying letters. Scrooge had a

---

implored: begged
bestow: to give
countinghouse: an office for business
court: a courtyard; an open space enclosed by walls or buildings
palpable: capable of being touched or felt
dismal: gloomy; dreary; hopeless

very small fire, but the clerk's fire was so very much smaller that it looked like one coal. But he couldn't replenish it, for Scrooge kept the coal-box in his own room; and so surely as the clerk came in with the shovel, the master predicted that it would be necessary for them to part. Wherefore the clerk put on his white comforter, and tried to warm himself at the candle; in which effort, not being a man of a strong imagination, he failed.

"A merry Christmas, uncle! God save you!" cried a cheerful voice. It was the voice of Scrooge's nephew, who came upon him so quickly that this was the first intimation he had of his approach.

"Bah!" said Scrooge, "Humbug!"

He had so heated himself with rapid walking in the fog and frost, this nephew of Scrooge's, that he was all in a glow; his face was ruddy and handsome; his eyes sparkled, and his breath smoked again. "Christmas a humbug, uncle!" said Scrooge's nephew. "You don't mean that, I am sure?"

"I do," said Scrooge. "Merry Christmas! What right have you to be merry? What reason have you to be merry? You're poor enough."

"Come, then," returned the nephew gaily. "What right have you to be dismal? What reason have you to be morose? You're rich enough."

Scrooge having no better answer ready on the spur of the moment, said "Bah!" again, and followed it up with, "Humbug."

---

replenish: to refill
comforter: a long scarf worn around the neck
intimation: a hint
humbug: nonsense; rubbish
morose: gloomy; glum

"Don't be cross, uncle!" said the nephew.

"What else can I be," returned the uncle, "when I live in such a world of fools as this? Merry Christmas! Out upon merry Christmas! What's Christmastime to you but a time for paying bills without money; a time for finding yourself a year older, but not an hour richer; a time for balancing your books and having every item in 'em through a round dozen of months presented dead against you? If I could work my will," said Scrooge indignantly, "every idiot who goes about with 'Merry Christmas' on his lips should be boiled with his own pudding, and buried with a stake of holly through his heart. He should!"

"Uncle!" pleaded the nephew.

"Nephew!" returned the uncle sternly, "keep Christmas in your own way, and let me keep it in mine."

"Keep it!" repeated Scrooge's nephew. "But you don't keep it."

"Let me leave it alone, then," said Scrooge. "Much good may it do you! Much good it has ever done you!"

"There are many things from which I might have derived good, by which I have not profited, I dare say," returned the nephew, "Christmas among the rest. But I am sure I have always thought of Christmastime as a good time—a kind, forgiving, charitable, pleasant time. And therefore, uncle, though it has never put a scrap of gold or silver in my pocket, I believe that it *has* done me good, and *will* do me good; and I say, God bless it!"

The clerk in the Tank involuntarily applauded.

---

indignantly: with anger, usually in response to something seen as wrong
　　or unjust
derived: gotten; received

Becoming immediately sensible of the impropriety, he poked the fire, and extinguished the last frail spark forever.

"Let me hear another sound from *you*," said Scrooge, " and you'll keep your Christmas by losing your situation! You're quite a powerful speaker, sir," he added, turning to his nephew. "I wonder you don't go into Parliament."

"Don't be angry, uncle. Come! Dine with us tomorrow." Scrooge said that he would see him—yes, indeed he did. He went the whole length of the expression, and said that he would see him in that extremity first.

"Good afternoon," said Scrooge.

His nephew left the room without an angry word, notwithstanding. He stopped at the outer door to bestow the greetings of the season on the clerk, who, cold as he was, was warmer than Scrooge, for he returned them cordially.

"There's another fellow," muttered Scrooge, who overheard him: "my clerk, with fifteen shillings a week, and a wife and family, talking about a merry Christmas. I'll retire to Bedlam."

This lunatic, in letting Scrooge's nephew out, had let two other people in. They were portly gentlemen, pleasant to behold, and now stood, with their hats off, in Scrooge's office. They had books and papers in their hands, and bowed to him.

---

sensible: aware
impropriety: the state of being improper, inappropriate, or unacceptable
situation: job; employment
Parliament: one branch of the English government, similar to Congress in the United States
extremity: farthest point
Bedlam: a hospital for the care of the insane
lunatic: an insane person (refers here to the clerk, whom Scrooge sees as crazy for celebrating Christmas even though he is poor)
portly: plump; fat

"Scrooge and Marley's, I believe," said one of the gentlemen, referring to his list. "Have I the pleasure of addressing Mr. Scrooge, or Mr. Marley?"

"Mr. Marley has been dead these seven years," Scrooge replied. "He died seven years ago, this very night."

"We have no doubt his liberality is well represented by his surviving partner," said the gentleman, presenting his credentials.

It certainly was; for they had been two kindred spirits. At the ominous word "liberality," Scrooge frowned, and shook his head, and handed the credentials back.

"At this festive season of the year, Mr. Scrooge," said the gentleman, taking up a pen, "it is more than usually desirable that we should make some slight provision for the poor and destitute, who suffer greatly at the present time. Many thousands are in want of common necessaries; hundreds of thousands are in want of common comforts, sir."

"Are there no prisons?" asked Scrooge.

"Plenty of prisons," said the gentleman, laying down the pen again.

"And the Union workhouses?" demanded Scrooge. "Are they still in operation?"

"They are. Still," returned the gentleman, "I wish I could say they were not."

---

liberality: generosity
credentials: official documents
kindred spirits: people who share similar beliefs and values
ominous: threatening; signaling danger
provision: the act of supplying or providing for
destitute: very poor people
in want of: in need of
Union workhouses: poorhouses (serving regions in England called "Unions"); places, often crowded and run-down, where poor people were given shelter and sometimes work to do

"The Treadmill and the Poor Law are in full vigor, then?" said Scrooge.

"Both very busy, sir."

"Oh! I was afraid, from what you said at first, that something had occurred to stop them in their useful course," said Scrooge. "I'm very glad to hear it. I don't make merry myself at Christmas and I can't afford to make idle people merry. I help to support the establishments I have mentioned—they cost enough; and those who are badly off must go there."

"Many can't go there; and many would rather die."

"If they would rather die," said Scrooge, "they had better do it, and decrease the surplus population. Good afternoon, gentlemen!"

Seeing clearly that it would be useless to pursue their point, the gentlemen withdrew.

At length the hour of shutting up the countinghouse arrived. With an ill-will Scrooge dismounted from his stool, and tacitly admitted the fact to the expectant clerk in the Tank, who instantly snuffed his candle out, and put on his hat.

"You'll want all day tomorrow, I suppose?" said Scrooge.

"If quite convenient, sir."

"It's not convenient," said Scrooge, "and it's not fair. If I was to stop half-a-crown for it, you'd think yourself ill-used, I'll be bound?"

---

Treadmill: a device once used for punishment in prisons, in which persons walked on the outer edge of a wide wheel

Poor Law: a law intended to help and reform the poor (but in Dickens's time, often ineffective)

surplus: extra; more than is needed

tacitly: without being spoken

crown: an old British coin

The clerk smiled faintly.

"And yet," said Scrooge, "you don't think *me* ill-used, when I pay a day's wages for no work."

The clerk observed that it was only once a year.

"A poor excuse for picking a man's pocket every twenty-fifth of December!" said Scrooge, buttoning his great-coat to the chin. "But I suppose you must have the whole day. Be here all the earlier next morning."

The clerk promised that he would, and Scrooge walked out with a growl. The office was closed in a twinkling, and the clerk, with the long ends of his white comforter dangling below his waist (for he boasted no great-coat), went down a slide on Cornhill, at the end of a lane of boys, twenty times, in honor of its being Christmas Eve, and then ran home to Camden Town as hard as he could pelt, to play at blindman's buff.

Scrooge took his melancholy dinner in his usual melancholy tavern; and having read all the newspapers, and beguiled the rest of the evening with his banker's book, went home to bed. He lived in chambers which had once belonged to his deceased partner. They were a gloomy suite of rooms, in a building that was old enough now, and dreary enough, for nobody lived in it but Scrooge, the other rooms being all let out as offices.

Now, it is a fact that there was nothing at all particular about the knocker on the door of this house, except that it was very large; also, that Scrooge had seen it, night and

---

pelt: to run; to move quickly
blindman's buff: a children's game in which one player is blindfolded and
    tries to catch the other players
melancholy: very sad; gloomy
beguiled: spent time pleasantly

morning, during his whole residence in that place; also, that Scrooge had as little of what is called fancy about him as any man in the city of London. And yet Scrooge, having his key in the lock of the door, saw in the knocker, without its undergoing any intermediate process of change, not a knocker, but Marley's face—Marley's face, with a dismal light about it, like a bad lobster in a dark cellar! It was not angry or ferocious, but it looked at Scrooge as Marley used to look, with ghostly spectacles turned up upon its ghostly forehead.

As Scrooge looked fixedly at this phenomenon, it was a knocker again. He said, "Pooh, pooh!" and closed the door with a bang.

The sound resounded through the house like thunder. Every room above, and every cask in the wine-merchant's cellars below, appeared to have a separate peal of echoes of its own. Scrooge was not a man to be frightened by echoes. He fastened the door, and walked across the hall, and up the stairs—slowly, too, trimming his candle as he went.

Up Scrooge went, not caring a button for its being very dark. Darkness is cheap, and Scrooge liked it. But before he shut his heavy door, he walked through his rooms to see that all was right. He had just enough recollection of the face to desire to do that.

Sitting room, bedroom, all were as they should be: nobody under the table, nobody under the sofa; a small fire in the grate; nobody under the bed; nobody in the closet; nobody in his dressing gown, which was hanging up in a suspicious attitude against the wall; old fire-guard, old shoes, two fish baskets, washing stand on three legs, and a poker.

fancy: imagination
phenomenon: an occurrence; a significant or unusual event
recollection: memory

Quite satisfied, he closed his door, and locked himself in; double-locked himself in, which was not his custom. Thus secured against surprise, he took off his cravat, put on his dressing gown and slippers and his nightcap, and sat down before the very low fire.

As he threw his head back in the chair, his glance happened to rest upon a bell, a disused bell, that hung in the room, and that communicated, for some purpose now forgotten, with a chamber in the highest story of the building. It was with great astonishment, and with a strange, inexplicable dread, that, as he looked, he saw this bell begin to swing. Soon it rang out loudly, and so did every bell in the house.

This was succeeded by a clanking noise, deep down below, as if some person were dragging a heavy chain over the casks in the wine-merchant's cellar.

Then he heard the noise grow much louder on the floors below; then coming up the stairs; then coming straight towards his door.

It came on through the heavy door, and a specter passed into the room before his eyes. And upon its coming in, the dying flame leaped up, as though it cried, "I know him! Marley's ghost!"

The same face, the very same!—Marley in his pigtail, usual waistcoat, tights, and boots. The chain he drew was clasped about his middle. It was made (for Scrooge observed it closely) of cash-boxes, keys, padlocks, ledgers, deeds, and heavy purses wrought in steel.

---

cravat: a necktie
inexplicable: not able to be explained
succeeded: followed
specter: spirit; ghost
waistcoat: vest

"How now!" said Scrooge, caustic and cold as ever. "What do you want with me?"

"Much!"—Marley's voice, no doubt about it.

"Who are you?"

"Ask me who I *was*."

"Who *were* you, then?"

"In life I was your partner, Jacob Marley."

"Can you—can you sit down?"

"I can."

"Do it, then."

The Ghost sat down on the opposite side of the fireplace, as if he were quite used to it.

"You don't believe in me," observed the Ghost.

"I don't," said Scrooge.

"What evidence would you have of my reality beyond that of your senses?"

"I don't know," said Scrooge.

"Why do you doubt your senses?"

"Because," said Scrooge, "a little thing affects them. A slight disorder of the stomach makes them cheats. You may be an undigested bit of beef, a blot of mustard, a crumb of cheese, a fragment of an underdone potato. Mercy! Dreadful apparition, why do you trouble me? Why do spirits walk the earth, and why do they come to me?"

---

caustic: bitterly sarcastic

apparition: an unusual sight; a ghost

"It is required of every man that the spirit within him should walk abroad among his fellow-men, and travel far and wide; and if that spirit goes not forth in life, it is condemned to do so after death. I cannot tell you all I would. A very little more is permitted to me. I cannot rest, I cannot stay, I cannot linger anywhere. My spirit never walked beyond our countinghouse—mark me!—in life my spirit never roved beyond the narrow limits of our money-changing hole; and weary journeys lie before me!"

"Seven years dead. And traveling all the time? You travel fast?"

"On the wings of the wind."

"You might have got over a great deal of ground in seven years."

"O blind man, blind man! Not to know that ages of incessant labor by immortal creatures for this earth must pass into eternity before the good of which it is susceptible is all developed. Not to know that any Christian spirit working kindly in its little sphere, whatever it may be, will find its mortal life too short for its vast means of usefulness. Not to know that no space of regret can make amends for one life's opportunities misused! Yet I was like this man; I once was like this man!"

"But you were always a good man of business, Jacob," faltered Scrooge, who now began to apply this to himself.

"Business!" cried the ghost, wringing its hands again. "Mankind was my business. The common welfare was my

---

condemned: doomed
roved: roamed; wandered
incessant: continual; unceasing
susceptible: open to; capable of being affected by
make amends: to make up for mistakes

business; charity, mercy, forbearance, benevolence, were all my business. The dealings of my trade were but a drop of water in the comprehensive ocean of my business."

Scrooge was very much dismayed to hear the specter going on at this rate, and began to quake exceedingly.

"Hear me! My time is nearly gone."

"I will. But don't be hard upon me, Jacob!"

"I am here tonight to warn you that you have yet a chance and hope of escaping my fate, Ebenezer."

"You were always a good friend to me," said Scrooge. "Thank-ee!"

"You will be haunted," resumed the Ghost, "by Three Spirits."

"Is that the chance and hope you mentioned, Jacob? I—I think I'd rather not."

"Without their visits, you cannot hope to shun the path I tread. Expect the first tomorrow night, when the bell tolls one. Expect the second on the next night at the same hour. The third, upon the next night, when the last stroke of twelve has ceased to vibrate. Look to see me no more; and look that, for your own sake, you remember what has passed between us!"

It walked backward from him; and at every step it took, the window raised itself a little, so that, when the apparition reached it, it was wide open.

Scrooge closed the window, and examined the door by which the Ghost had entered. It was double-locked, as he had locked it with his own hands, and the bolts were undisturbed. Scrooge tried to say, "Humbug!" but stopped at

---

forbearance: patience; tolerance
benevolence: kindness
comprehensive: complete, wide in scope
shun: to avoid

the first syllable. And being, from the emotion he had undergone, or the fatigues of the day, or his glimpse of the invisible world, or the dull conversation of the Ghost, or the lateness of the hour, much in need of repose, he went straight to bed, without undressing, and fell asleep on the instant.

## STAVE II: THE FIRST OF THE THREE SPIRITS

When Scrooge awoke, it was so dark, that, looking out of bed, he could scarcely distinguish the transparent window from the opaque walls of his chamber, until suddenly the church clock tolled a deep, dull, hollow, melancholy One.

Light flashed up in the room upon the instant, and the curtains of his bed were drawn aside by a strange figure— like a child, yet not so like a child as like an old man, viewed through some supernatural medium, which gave him the appearance of having receded from the view, and being diminished to a child's proportions. Its hair, which hung about its neck and down its back, was white as if with age; and yet the face had not a wrinkle in it, and the tenderest bloom was on the skin. It held a branch of fresh green holly in its hand; and, in singular contradiction of that wintry emblem, had its dress trimmed with summer flowers. But the strangest thing about it was, that from the crown of its head there sprang a bright clear jet of light, by which all this was visible; and which was doubtless the occasion of its using, in its duller moments, a great extinguisher for a cap, which it now held under its arm.

repose: rest
opaque: unclear; not transparent
receded: moved away; withdrawn; grown smaller
diminished: decreased; lessened
emblem: a sign or symbol

"Are you the Spirit, sir, whose coming was foretold to me?" asked Scrooge.

"I am." The voice was soft and gentle, as if it were at a distance.

"Who and what are you?"

"I am the Ghost of Christmas Past."

"Long past?" inquired Scrooge.

"No. Your past. The things that you will see with me are shadows of the things that have been; they will have no consciousness of us."

Scrooge then made bold to inquire what business brought him there.

"Your welfare. Rise, and walk with me!"

It would have been in vain for Scrooge to plead that the weather and the hour were not adapted to pedestrian purposes; that the bed was warm, and the thermometer a long way below freezing; that he was clad but lightly in his slippers, dressing gown, and nightcap; and that he had a cold upon him at that time. The grasp, though gentle as a woman's hand, was not to be resisted. He arose; but, finding that the Spirit made towards the window, he clasped its robe in supplication.

"I am a mortal," Scrooge protested, "and liable to fall."

"Bear but a touch of my hand *there*," said the Spirit, laying it upon his heart, "and you shall be upheld in more than this."

As the words were spoken, they passed through the wall, and stood in the busy thoroughfares of a city. It was made plain enough by the dressing of the shops that here, too, it was Christmas time.

---

consciousness: awareness
pedestrian: having to do with walking
supplication: begging or pleading
thoroughfares: main roads

The Ghost stopped at a certain warehouse door, and asked Scrooge whether he knew it.

"Know it! I was apprenticed here!"

They went in. At sight of an old gentleman in a Welsh wig, sitting behind such a high desk that, if he had been two inches taller, he must have knocked his head against the ceiling, Scrooge cried in great excitement, "Why, it's old Fezziwig! Bless his heart, it's Fezziwig, alive again!"

Old Fezziwig laid down his pen and looked up at the clock, which pointed to the hour of seven. He rubbed his hands, adjusted his capacious waistcoat, laughed all over himself, from his shoes to his organ of benevolence, and called out in a comfortable, oily, rich, fat, jovial voice, "Yo ho, there! Ebenezer! Dick!"

A living and moving picture of Scrooge's former self, a young man, came briskly in, accompanied by his fellow 'prentice.

"Dick Wilkins, to be sure!" said Scrooge to the Ghost. "My old fellow 'prentice! Bless me, yes. There he is. He was very much attached to me, was Dick. Poor Dick! Dear, dear!"

"Yo ho, my boys!" said Fezziwig. "No more work tonight. Christmas eve, Dick! Christmas, Ebenezer! Let's have the shutters up, before a man can say Jack Robinson! Clear away, my lads, and let's have lots of room here!"

Clear away! There was nothing they wouldn't have cleared away, or couldn't have cleared away, with old Fezziwig looking on. It was done in a minute. Every movable was packed off, as if it were dismissed from public life forevermore; the floor was swept and watered, the lamps were trimmed, fuel was heaped upon the fire; and the

capacious: roomy; having space
'prentice: short for *apprentice,* someone who learns a trade from an expert

warehouse became as snug and warm and dry and bright a ballroom as you would desire to see upon a winter's night.

In came a fiddler with a music-book, and went up to the lofty desk, and made an orchestra of it. In came Mrs. Fezziwig, one vast, substantial smile. In came the three Miss Fezziwigs, beaming and lovable. In came the six young followers whose hearts they had broken. In came all the young men and women employed in the business. In came the housemaid, with her cousin the baker. In came the cook, with her brother's particular friend the milkman. In they all came, one after another; some shyly, some boldly, some gracefully, some awkwardly, some pushing, some pulling; in they all came, anyhow and everyhow. Away they all went, twenty couples at once; hands half round and back again the other way; down the middle and up again; round and round in various stages of affectionate grouping; old top couple always turning up in the wrong place; new top couple starting off again, as soon as they got there; all top couples at last, and not a bottom one to help them. When this result was brought about, old Fezziwig, clapping his hands to stop the dance, cried out, "Well done!"

There were more dances, and there were forfeits, and then more dances; and there was cake, and there was a great piece of Cold Roast, and there was a great piece of Cold Boiled, and there were mince pies. But the great effect of the evening came after the Roast and Boiled, when the fiddler struck up "Sir Roger de Coverley." Then old Fezziwig stood out to dance with Mrs. Fezziwig. Top couple, too; with a good stiff piece of work cut out for them; three or four and twenty pair of partners; people who were not to be trifled with; people who *would* dance, and who had no notion of walking.

---

forfeits: a game in which things are given up

But if they had been twice as many—four times—as old, Fezziwig would have been a match for them, and so would Mrs. Fezziwig. As to her, she was worthy to be his partner in every sense of the term. A positive light appeared to issue from Fezziwig's calves. They shone in every part of the dance. You couldn't have predicted, at any given time, what would become of 'em next. And when old Fezziwig and Mrs. Fezziwig had gone all through the dance—advance and retire, turn your partner, bow and courtesy, corkscrew, thread the needle, and back again to your place—Fezziwig "cut,"—cut so deftly, that he appeared to wink with his legs.

When the clock struck eleven, this domestic ball broke up. Mr. and Mrs. Fezziwig took their stations, one on each side the door; and, shaking hands with every person individually as he or she went out, wished him or her a Merry Christmas. When everybody had retired but the two 'prentices, they did the same to them; and thus the cheerful voices died away, and the lads were left to their beds, which were under a counter in the back shop.

"A small matter," said the Ghost, "to make these silly folks so full of gratitude. He has spent but a few pounds of your mortal money—three or four perhaps. Is that so much that he deserves this praise?"

"It isn't that," said Scrooge, heated by the remark, and speaking unconsciously like his former, not his latter, self—"it isn't that, Spirit. He has the power to render us happy or unhappy; to make our service light or burdensome, a pleasure or a toil. Say that his power lies in words and looks; in things so slight and insignificant that it is impossible to

deftly: skillfully
render: to make

add and count 'em up; what then? The happiness he gives is quite as great as if it cost a fortune."

He felt the Spirit's glance, and stopped.

"What is the matter?" asked the Spirit.

"Nothing in particular," said Scrooge.

"Something, I think?" the Ghost insisted.

"No," said Scrooge, "no. I should like to be able to say a word or two to my clerk just now. That's all."

"My time grows short," observed the Spirit. "Quick!"

"Spirit!" said Scrooge in a broken voice. "Remove me from this place."

"I told you these were shadows of the things that have been," said the Ghost. "That they are what they are, do not blame me!"

"Remove me!" Scrooge exclaimed. "I cannot bear it! Leave me! Take me back. Haunt me no longer!"

As he struggled with the Spirit, he was conscious of being exhausted and overcome by an irresistible drowsiness; and, further, of being in his own bedroom. He had barely time to reel to bed before he sank into a heavy sleep.

## STAVE III: THE SECOND OF THE THREE SPIRITS

Scrooge awoke in his own bedroom. There was no doubt about that. But it and his own adjoining sitting room, into which he shuffled in his slippers, attracted by a great light there, had undergone a surprising transformation. The walls and ceiling were so hung with living green that it looked a perfect grove. The leaves of holly, mistletoe, and ivy reflected back the light, as if so many little mirrors had been scattered there; and such a mighty blaze went roaring up the chimney as that hearth had never known in Scrooge's time, or

Marley's or for many and many a winter season gone. Heaped upon the floor, to form a kind of throne, were turkeys, geese, game, great joints of meat, mince pies, plum puddings, barrels of oysters, red-hot chestnuts, cherry-cheeked apples, juicy oranges, luscious pears, and immense twelfth-cakes. In easy state upon the couch, there sat a Giant glorious to see, who bore a glowing torch, in shape not unlike Plenty's horn, and who raised it high to shed its light on Scrooge, as he came peeping round the door.

"Come in—come in, and know me better, man! I am the Ghost of Christmas Present. Look upon me! You have never seen the like of me before!"

"Never," Scrooge answered.

"Have you never walked forth with the younger members of my family; meaning (for I am very young) my elder brothers born in these later years?" pursued the Phantom.

"I don't think I have; I am afraid I have not. Have you had many brothers, Spirit?"

"More than eighteen hundred."

"A tremendous family to provide for!" muttered Scrooge. "Spirit, conduct me where you will. I went forth last night on compulsion, and I learnt a lesson which is working now. Tonight, if you have aught to teach me, let me profit by it."

"Touch my robe!"

Scrooge did as he was told, and held it fast.

The room and its contents all vanished instantly, and they stood in the city streets upon a snowy Christmas morning.

Scrooge and the Ghost passed on, invisible, straight to Scrooge's clerk's; and on the threshold of the door the Spirit

---

Plenty's horn: a horn of plenty; a cornucopia
on compulsion: by force
aught: anything

smiled, and stopped to bless Bob Cratchit's dwelling with the
sprinklings of his torch. Think of that! Bob had but fifteen
"Bob" a week himself; he pocketed on Saturdays but fifteen
copies of his Christian name; and yet the Ghost of Christmas
Present blessed his four-roomed house!

Then up rose Mrs. Cratchit, Cratchit's wife, dressed out but
poorly in a twice-turned gown, but brave in ribbons, which
though cheap make a goodly show for sixpence; and she laid
the cloth, assisted by Belinda Cratchit, second of her
daughters, also brave in ribbons; while Master Peter Cratchit

bob: an English coin

plunged a fork into the saucepan of potatoes, and, getting the corners of his monstrous shirt collar (Bob's private property, conferred upon his son and heir in honor of the day) into his mouth, rejoiced to find himself so gallantly attired, and yearned to show his linen in the fashionable Parks. And now two smaller Cratchits, boy and girl, came tearing in, screaming that outside the baker's they had smelt the goose, and had known it for their own. Basking in luxurious thoughts of sage and onion, these young Cratchits danced about the table, and exalted Master Peter Cratchit to the skies, while he (not proud, although his collars nearly choked him) blew the fire, until the slow potatoes, bubbling up, knocked loudly at the saucepan lid to be let out and peeled.

"What has ever got your precious father, then?" said Mrs. Cratchit. "And your brother, Tiny Tim! And Martha wasn't so late last Christmas day by half an hour!"

"Here's Martha, Mother!" said a girl, appearing as she spoke.

"Here's Martha, Mother!" cried the two young Cratchits. "Hurrah! There's *such* a goose, Martha!"

"Why, bless your heart alive, my dear, how late you are!" said Mrs. Cratchit, kissing her a dozen times, and taking off her shawl and bonnet for her.

"We'd a deal of work to finish up last night," replied the girl, "and I had to clear away this morning, Mother!"

"Well! Never mind so long as you are come," said Mrs. Cratchit. "Sit ye down before the fire, my dear, and have a warm, Lord bless ye!"

---

conferred upon: given to
gallantly: stylishly; dashingly
luxurious: full of ease and comfort
exalted: praised

"No, no! There's Father coming," cried the two young Cratchits, who were everywhere at once. "Hide, Martha, hide!"

So Martha hid herself, and in came little Bob, the father, with at least three feet of comforter, exclusive of the fringe, hanging down before him; and his threadbare clothes darned up and brushed, to look seasonable; and Tiny Tim upon his shoulder.

Alas for Tiny Tim, he bore a little crutch, and had his limbs supported by an iron frame!

"Why, where's our Martha?" cried Bob Cratchit, looking round.

"Not coming," said Mrs. Cratchit.

"Not coming!" said Bob, with a sudden declension of his high spirits; for he had been Tim's horse all the way from church, and had come home rampant—"not coming upon Christmas day!"

Martha didn't like to see him disappointed, even if it were only in a joke; so she came out prematurely from behind the closet door, and ran into his arms, while the two young Cratchits hustled Tiny Tim, and bore him off into the washhouse that he might hear the pudding singing in the copper.

"And how did little Tim behave?" asked Mrs. Cratchit, when she had rallied Bob on his credulity, and Bob had hugged his daughter to his heart's content.

---

declension: a decrease

rampant: a term used to describe a four-legged animal, such as a horse or lion, rearing up on its hind legs and extending its forelegs

pudding: dessert

copper: a cooking pot

credulity: the characteristic of being too ready to believe whatever one is told

"As good as gold," said Bob, "and better. Somehow he gets thoughtful, sitting by himself so much, and thinks the strangest things you ever heard. He told me, coming home, that he hoped the people saw him in the church, because he was a cripple, and it might be pleasant to them to remember, upon Christmas day, who made lame beggars walk and blind men see."

Bob's voice was tremulous when he told them this, and it trembled more when he said that Tiny Tim was growing strong and hearty.

His active little crutch was heard upon the floor, and back came Tiny Tim before another word was spoken, escorted by his brother and sister to his stool beside the fire; and while Bob, turning up his cuffs—as if, poor fellow, they were capable of being made more shabby—compounded some hot mixture in a jug, and stirred it round and round and put it on the hob to simmer, Master Peter and the two ubiquitous young Cratchits went to fetch the goose, with which they soon returned in high procession.

Mrs. Cratchit made the gravy (ready beforehand in a little saucepan) hissing hot; Master Peter mashed the potatoes with incredible vigor; Miss Belinda sweetened up the applesauce; Martha dusted the hot plates; Bob took Tiny Tim beside him in a tiny corner at the table; the two young Cratchits set chairs for everybody, not forgetting themselves, and mounting guard upon their posts, crammed spoons into their mouths, lest they should shriek for goose before their turn came to be helped. At last the dishes were set on, and

tremulous: shaky
hob: at the back of a fireplace, a shelf on which to keep things warm
ubiquitous: seeming to be everywhere at once
vigor: strength; energy
lest: for fear that

grace was said. It was succeeded by a breathless pause, as Mrs. Cratchit, looking slowly all along the carving-knife, prepared to plunge it in the breast; but when she did, and when the long-expected gush of stuffing issued forth, one murmur of delight arose all round the board, and even Tiny Tim, excited by the two young Cratchits, beat on the table with the handle of his knife, and feebly cried, "Hurrah!"

There never was such a goose. Bob said he didn't believe there ever was such a goose cooked. Its tenderness and flavor, size and cheapness, were the themes of universal admiration. Eked out by applesauce and mashed potatoes, it was a sufficient dinner for the whole family; indeed, as Mrs. Cratchit said with great delight (surveying one small atom of a bone upon the dish), "they hadn't ate it all at last!" Yet everyone had had enough, and the youngest Cratchits in particular were steeped in sage and onion to the eyebrows! But now, the plates being changed by Miss Belinda, Mrs. Cratchit left the room alone—too nervous to bear witnesses—to take the pudding up, and bring it in.

Suppose it should not be done enough! Suppose it should break in turning out! Suppose somebody should have got over the wall of the back yard, and stolen it, while they were merry with the goose—a supposition at which the two young Cratchits became livid! All sorts of horrors were supposed.

Hallo! A great deal of steam! The pudding was out of the copper. A smell like a washing-day! That was the cloth. A smell like an eating house and a pastry cook's next door to

---

eked out: increased; made to last little by little
surveying: observing
supposition: something that has been supposed; an assumption
livid: very angry; furious

each other, with the laundress's next door to that! That was the pudding! In half a minute Mrs. Cratchit entered—flushed but smiling proudly—with the pudding, like a speckled cannonball, so hard and firm, and bedight with Christmas holly stuck into the top.

Oh, a wonderful pudding! Bob Cratchit said, and calmly, too, that he regarded it as the greatest success achieved by Mrs. Cratchit since their marriage. Mrs. Cratchit said that now the weight was off her mind, she would confess she had had her doubts about the quantity of flour. Everybody had something to say about it, but nobody said or thought it was at all a small pudding for a large family. Any Cratchit would have blushed to hint at such a thing.

At last the dinner was all done, the cloth was cleared, the hearth swept, and the fire made up. The compound in the jug being tasted and considered perfect, apples and oranges were put upon the table, and a shovelful of chestnuts on the fire.

Then all the Cratchit family drew round the hearth, in what Bob Cratchit called a circle, and at Bob Cratchit's elbow stood the family display of glass—two tumblers, and a custard-cup without a handle.

These held the hot stuff from the jug, however, as well as golden goblets would have done; and Bob served it out with beaming looks, while the chestnuts on the fire sputtered and crackled noisily. Then Bob proposed: "A Merry Christmas to us all, my dears. God bless us!"

Which all the family echoed.

"God bless us every one!" said Tiny Tim, the last of all.

He sat very close to his father's side, upon his little stool. Bob held his withered little hand in his, as if he loved the

bedight: dressed or decorated with
withered: shriveled

child, and wished to keep him by his side, and dreaded that he might be taken from him.

"Spirit," said Scrooge, with an interest he had never felt before, "tell me if Tiny Tim will live."

"I see a vacant seat," replied the Ghost, "in the poor chimney-corner, and a crutch without an owner. If these shadows remain unaltered by the Future, the child will die."

"No, no," said Scrooge. "Oh, no, kind Spirit. Say he will be spared." Scrooge cast his eyes upon the ground. But he raised them speedily, on hearing his own name.

"Mr. Scrooge!" said Bob; "I'll give you Mr. Scrooge, the Founder of the Feast!"

"The Founder of the Feast, indeed!" cried Mrs. Cratchit, reddening. "I wish I had him here. I'd give him a piece of my mind to feast upon, and I hope he'd have a good appetite for it."

"My dear," said Bob, "the children! Christmas day."

"It should be Christmas day, I am sure," said she, "on which one drinks the health of such an odious, stingy, hard, unfeeling man as Mr. Scrooge. You know he is, Robert! Nobody knows it better than you do, poor fellow!"

"My dear," was Bob's mild answer, "Christmas day."

"I'll drink his health for your sake and the day's," said Mrs. Cratchit, "not for his. Long life to him. A Merry Christmas and a happy new year! He'll be very merry and very happy, I have no doubt!"

The children drank the toast after her. It was the first of their proceedings which had no heartiness in it. Tiny Tim drank it last of all, but he didn't care twopence for it. Scrooge was the Ogre of the family. The mention of his name cast a

---

odious: hateful; extremely unpleasant

dark shadow on the party, which was not dispelled for a full five minutes.

After it had passed away, they were ten times merrier than before, from the mere relief of Scrooge the Baleful being done with. Bob Cratchit told them how he had a situation in his eye for Master Peter, which would bring in, if obtained, full five and sixpence weekly. The two young Cratchits laughed tremendously at the idea of Peter's being a man of business; and Peter himself looked thoughtfully at the fire from between his collars, as if he were deliberating what particular investments he should favor when he came into the receipt of that bewildering income. Martha, who was a poor apprentice at a milliner's, then told them what kind of work she had to do, and how many hours she worked at a stretch, and how she meant to lie abed tomorrow morning for a good long rest; tomorrow being a holiday, she could pass it at home. Also how she had seen a countess and a lord some days before, and how the lord "was much about as tall as Peter"; at which Peter pulled up his collars so high that you couldn't have seen his head if you had been there. All this time the chestnuts and the jug went round and round; and by and by they had a song, about a lost child traveling in the snow, from Tiny Tim, who had a plaintive little voice, and who sang it very well indeed.

There was nothing of high mark in this. They were not a handsome family; they were not well dressed; their shoes were far from being waterproof; their clothes were scanty;

dispelled: driven away
baleful: harmful; threatening evil
situation: a job
milliner: a hatmaker
plaintive: sorrowful; mournful
scanty: few; not enough; barely adequate

and Peter might have known, and very likely did, the inside of a pawnbroker's. But they were happy, grateful, pleased with one another, and contented with the time; and when they faded, and looked happier yet in the bright sprinklings of the Spirit's torch at parting, Scrooge had his eye upon them, and especially on Tiny Tim, until the last.

It was a great surprise to Scrooge, as this scene vanished, to hear a hearty laugh. It was a much greater surprise to Scrooge to recognize it as his own nephew's, and to find himself in a bright, dry, gleaming room, with the Spirit standing smiling by his side, and looking at that same nephew.

It is a fair, even-handed, noble adjustment of things, that while there is infection in disease and sorrow, there is nothing in the world so irresistibly contagious as laughter and good humor. When Scrooge's nephew laughed, Scrooge's niece by marriage laughed as heartily as he. And their assembled friends, being not a bit behindhand, laughed out lustily.

"He said that Christmas was a humbug, as I live!" cried Scrooge's nephew. "He believed it, too!"

"More shame for him, Fred!" said Scrooge's niece, indignantly. Bless those women! They never do anything by halves. They are always in earnest.

She was very pretty, exceedingly pretty. With a dimpled, surprised-looking, capital face; all kinds of good little dots about her chin, that melted into one another when she

---

irresistibly: in a way that cannot be opposed or resisted

lustily: heartily; with great enthusiasm

indignantly: in a way that shows anger in response to something mean or unjust

in earnest: serious; sincere

capital: very fine; excellent

laughed; and the sunniest pair of eyes that you ever saw in any little creature's head.

"He's a comical old fellow," said Scrooge's nephew, "that's the truth, and not so pleasant as he might be. However, his offenses carry their own punishment, and I have nothing to say against him. Who suffers by his ill whims? Himself, always. Here he takes it into his head to dislike us, and he won't come and dine with us. What's the consequence? He doesn't lose much of a dinner."

"Indeed, I think he loses a very good dinner," interrupted Scrooge's niece. Everybody else said the same, and they must be allowed to have been competent judges, because they had just had dinner; and, with the dessert upon the table, were clustered round the fire, by lamplight.

"Well, I am very glad to hear it," said Scrooge's nephew, "because I haven't any great faith, in these young housekeepers. What do you say, Topper?"

Topper clearly had his eye on one of Scrooge's niece's sisters, for he answered that a bachelor was a wretched outcast, who had no right to express an opinion on the subject. Whereat Scrooge's niece's sister, the plump one, with the lace tucker, not the one with the roses, blushed.

After tea they had some music; for they were a musical family, and they knew what they were about when they sang a Glee or Catch, I can assure you—especially Topper, who could growl away in the bass like a good one, and never swell the large veins in his forehead, or get red in the face over it.

But they didn't devote the whole evening to music. After a while they played at forfeits; for it is good to be children

---

tucker: a collar

sometimes, and never better than at Christmas, when its mighty Founder was a child himself. There was first a game at blind-man's-buff, though. And I no more believe Topper was really blinded than I believe he had his eyes in his boots. Because the way in which he went after that plump sister in the lace tucker was an outrage on the credulity of human nature. Knocking down the fire irons, tumbling over the chairs, bumping up against the piano, smothering himself among the curtains, wherever she went, there went he! He always knew where the plump sister was. He wouldn't catch anybody else. If you had fallen up against him, as some of them did, and stood there, he would have made a feint of endeavoring to seize you, which would have been an affront to your understanding, and would instantly have sidled off in the direction of the plump sister.

"Here is a new game," said Scrooge. "One half hour, Spirit, only one!"

It was a game called Yes and No, where Scrooge's nephew had to think of something, and the rest must find out what, he answering only to their questions yes or no, as the case was. The fire of questioning to which he was exposed elicited from him that he was thinking of an animal, a live animal, rather a disagreeable animal, a savage animal, an animal that growled and grunted sometimes, and talked sometimes, and lived in London, and walked about the streets, and wasn't made a show of, and wasn't led by anybody, and didn't live in a menagerie, and was never killed in the

---

feint: a pretend movement
endeavoring: trying
affront: insult
sidled: moved sideways, especially in a sneaky way
elicited: drew out
menagerie: a collection of animals

market, and was not a horse, or a donkey, or a cow, or a tiger, or a dog, or a pig, or a cat, or a bear. At every new question put to him, this nephew burst into a fresh roar of laughter, and was so inexpressibly tickled that he was obliged to get up off the sofa and stamp. At last the plump sister cried out—

"I have found it out! I know what it is, Fred! I know what it is!"

"What is it?" cried Fred.

"It's your uncle, Scro-o-o-o-oge!"

Which it certainly was. Admiration was the universal sentiment, though some objected that the reply to "Is it a bear?" ought to have been "Yes."

Uncle Scrooge had imperceptibly become so gay and light of heart that he would have drunk to the unconscious company in an inaudible speech. But the whole scene passed off in the breath of the last word spoken by his nephew; and he and the Spirit were again upon their travels.

Much they saw, and far they went, and many homes they visited, but always with a happy end. The Spirit stood beside sick beds, and they were cheerful; on foreign lands, and they were close at home; by struggling men, and they were patient in their greater hope; by poverty, and it was rich. In almshouse, hospital, and jail, in misery's every refuge, where vain man in his little brief authority had not made fast the door, and barred the Spirit out, he left his blessing, and taught Scrooge his precepts. Suddenly, as they stood together in an open place, the bell struck twelve.

imperceptibly: without being noticed
unconscious: unaware
inaudible: not able to be heard
almshouse: a place for very poor people to live
precepts: rules; principles

Scrooge looked about him for the Ghost, and saw it no more. As the last stroke ceased to vibrate, he remembered the prediction of old Jacob Marley, and, lifting up his eyes, beheld a solemn Phantom, draped and hooded, coming like a mist along the ground towards him.

## STAVE IV: THE LAST OF THE SPIRITS

The Phantom slowly, gravely, silently approached. When it came near him, Scrooge bent down upon his knee; for in the air through which this Spirit moved, it seemed to scatter gloom and mystery.

It was shrouded in a deep black garment, which concealed its head, its face, its form, and left nothing of it visible save one outstretched hand. He knew no more, for the Spirit neither spoke nor moved.

"I am in the presence of the Ghost of Christmas yet to come," said Scrooge. "Ghost of the Future! I fear you more than any specter I have seen. But as I know your purpose is to do me good, and as I hope to live to be another man from what I was, I am prepared to bear you company, and do it with a thankful heart. Will you not speak to me?"

The Spirit answered not, but pointed onward with its hand.

"Lead on!" said Scrooge. "Lead on! The night is waning fast, and it is precious time to me, I know. Lead on, Spirit!"

They hardly seemed to enter the city, for the city rather seemed to spring up about them. But there they were in the heart of it, on 'Change, amongst the merchants.

The Spirit stopped beside one little knot of businessmen. Observing that the hand was pointed to them, Scrooge advanced to listen to their talk.

---

waning: decreasing, approaching its end

"No," said a great fat man with a monstrous chin, "I don't know much about it either way. I only know he's dead."

"When did he die?" inquired another.

"Last night, I believe."

"Why, what was the matter with him? I thought he'd never die."

"What has he done with his money?" asked a red-faced gentleman.

"I haven't heard," said the man with the large chin. "Company, perhaps. He hasn't left it to me. That's all I know."

This pleasantry was received with a general laugh.

"It's likely to be a very cheap funeral," said the same speaker; "for upon my life I don't know of anybody to go to it. Suppose we make up a party and volunteer?"

"I don't mind going if a lunch is provided," observed the red-faced gentleman. "But I must be fed."

Another laugh.

"Spirit!" said Scrooge, shuddering from head to foot. "I see, I see. The case of this unhappy man might be my own. My life tends that way now. Merciful heaven, what is this!"

He recoiled in terror, for the scene had changed, and now he almost touched a bare, uncurtained bed, on which, beneath a ragged sheet, there lay something covered up. A pale light, rising in the outer air, fell straight upon this bed; and on it, unwatched, unwept, uncared for, was the body of an unknown man.

He lay in the dark empty house, with not a man, a woman, or a child to say that he was kind to me in this or that. A cat was tearing at the door, and there was a sound of gnawing rats beneath the hearthstone. What they wanted in the room of death, and why they were so restless and disturbed, Scrooge did not dare to think.

"Spirit!" he said. "This is a fearful place. In leaving it, I shall not leave its lesson, trust me. Let us go!"

The Phantom spread its dark robe before him for a moment, like a wing; and withdrawing it, revealed poor Bob Cratchit's house, the dwelling he had visited before. He found the mother and the children seated round the fire.

Quiet. Very quiet. The noisy little Cratchits were as still as statues in one corner, and sat looking up at Peter, who had a book before him. The mother and her daughters were engaged in sewing. But surely they were very quiet!

The mother laid her work upon the table, and put her hand up to her face.

"The color hurts my eyes," she said.

The color? Ah, poor Tiny Tim!

"They're better now again," said Cratchit's wife. "It makes them weak by candlelight, and I wouldn't show weak eyes to your father when he comes home, for the world. It must be near his time."

"Past it rather," Peter answered, shutting up his book. "But I think he has walked a little slower these last few evenings, mother."

They were very quiet again. At least she said, and in a steady, cheerful voice, that only faltered once, "I have known him walk with—I have known him walk with Tiny Tim upon his shoulder, very fast indeed."

"And so have I," cried Peter. "Often."

"And so have I," exclaimed another. So had all.

"But he was very light to carry," she resumed, intent upon her work, "and his father loved him so, that it was no trouble—no trouble. And there is your father at the door!"

She hurried out to meet him, and little Bob came in. His tea was ready, and they all tried who should help him to it the most. Then the two young Cratchits got upon his knees and each child laid a little cheek upon his face, as if they had said, "Don't mind it, father. Don't be grieved!"

Bob was very cheerful with them, and spoke pleasantly to all the family. He looked at the work upon the table, and praised the industry and speed of Mrs. Cratchit and the girls. They would be done long before Sunday, he said.

"Sunday! You went today then, Robert?" said his wife.

"Yes, my dear," returned Bob. "I wish you could have gone. It would have done you good to see how green a place it is. But you'll see it often. I promised him that I would walk there on a Sunday. My little, little child!" cried Bob. "My little child!"

He broke down all at once. He left the room and went upstairs into the room above, and when he thought a little and had composed himself, he was reconciled to what had happened, and went down again.

They drew about the fire and talked. "However and whenever we part from one another," said Bob, "I am sure we shall none of us ever forget poor Tiny Tim—shall we—or this first paring that there was among us?"

"Never, father!" cried they all.

"Specter," said Scrooge, "something informs me that our parting moment is at hand. I know it, but I know not how. Tell me what man that was, with the covered face, whom we saw lying dead?"

The Ghost of Christmas Yet to Come conveyed him to a dismal, wretched, ruinous churchyard.

The Spirit stood among the graves, and pointed down to one.

---

reconciled: having accepted or submitted to something difficult
    or unpleasant

"Before I draw nearer to that stone to which you point," said Scrooge, "answer me one question. Are these the shadows of the things that will be, or are they shadows of the things that may be only?"

Still the Ghost pointed downward to the grave by which it stood.

"Men's courses will foreshadow certain ends, to which, if persevered in, they must lead," said Scrooge. "But if the courses be departed from, the ends will change. Say it is thus with what you show me!"

The Spirit was immovable as ever.

Scrooge crept towards it, trembling as he went; and, following the finger, read upon the stone of the neglected grave his own name—*Ebenezer Scrooge.*

foreshadow: to hint at what will happen
persevered: continued

"Am I that man who lay upon the bed? No, Spirit! Oh no, no! Spirit! Hear me! I am not the man I was. I will not be the man I must have been but for this. Why show me this, if I am past all hope? Assure me that I yet may change these shadows you have shown me by an altered life."

For the first time the kind hand faltered.

"I will honor Christmas in my heart, and try to keep it all the year. I will live in the Past, the Present, and the Future. The Spirits of all three shall strive within me. I will not shut out the lessons that they teach. Oh, tell me I may sponge away the writing on this stone!"

Holding up his hands in one last prayer to have his fate reversed, he saw an alteration in the Phantom's hood and dress. It shrank, collapsed, and dwindled down into a bedpost.

Yes, and the bedpost was his own. The bed was his own, and the room was his own. Best and happiest of all, the time before him was his own, to make amends in!

He was checked in his transports by the churches ringing out the lustiest peals he had ever heard.

Running to the window, he opened it, and put out his head. No fog, no mist, no night; clear, bright, stirring, golden day!

"What's today?" cried Scrooge, calling downward to a boy in Sunday clothes, who perhaps had loitered in to look about him.

"Eh?" returned the boy.

"What's today, my fine fellow?" said Scrooge.

"Today! Why, Christmas day," replied the boy.

"It's Christmas day! I haven't missed it. Hallo, my fine fellow!"

---

alteration: a change
checked: stopped
transports: powerful (and usually happy) emotions
lustiest: most energetic and enthusiastic

"Hallo!" returned the boy.

"Do you know the poulterer's, in the next street but one, at the corner?" Scrooge inquired.

"I should hope I did," replied the lad.

"An intelligent boy! A remarkable boy! Do you know whether they've sold the prize turkey that was hanging up there? Not the little prize turkey—the big one?"

"What, the one as big as me?"

"What a delightful boy! It's a pleasure to talk to him. Yes, my boy!"

"It's hanging there now."

"Is it? Go and buy it. I am in earnest. Go and buy it, and tell 'em to bring it here, that I may give them the direction where to take it. Come back with the man, and I'll give you a shilling. Come back with him in less than five minutes, and I'll give you half a crown!"

The boy was off like a shot.

"I'll send it to Bob Cratchit's!" said Scrooge with a laugh. "He shan't know who sends it. It's twice the size of Tiny Tim!"

The hand in which he wrote the address was not a steady one; but write it he did, somehow, and went downstairs to open the street door, ready for the coming of the poulterer's man.

It *was* a turkey! He never could have stood upon his legs, that bird. He would have snapped 'em short off in a minute, like sticks of sealing wax.

Scrooge dressed himself "all in his best," and at last got out into the streets. The people were by this time pouring forth, as he had seen them with the Ghost of Christmas Present; and, walking with his hands behind him, Scrooge regarded every one with a delighted smile. He looked so irresistibly pleasant, in a word, that three or four good-humored fellows said,

poulterer: someone who sells poultry, such as chickens and turkeys

"Good morning, sir! A Merry Christmas to you!" and Scrooge said often afterwards, that, of all the blithe sounds he had ever heard, those were the blithest in his ears.

In the afternoon he turned his steps towards his nephew's house.

He passed the door a dozen times before he had the courage to go up and knock. But he made a dash, and did it.

"Is your master at home, my dear?" said Scrooge to the girl.

"Yes, sir."

"Where is he?"

"He's in the dining room, sir, along with Mistress."

"He knows me," said Scrooge, with his hand already on the dining room lock, "I'll go in here."

He turned it gently and sidled his face in, round the door. They were looking at the table (which was spread out in great array); for these young housekeepers are always nervous on such points, and like to see that everything is right.

"Fred!" said Scrooge.

"Why, bless my soul!" cried Fred. "Who's that?"

"It's I. Your uncle Scrooge. I have come to dinner. Will you let me in, Fred?"

Let him in! It is a mercy he didn't shake his arm off. He was at home in five minutes. Nothing could be heartier. His niece looked just the same. So did Topper when *he* came. So did the plump sister when *she* came. So did every one when *they* came. Wonderful party, wonderful games, wonderful unanimity, won-der-ful happiness!

But he was early at the office next morning. Oh, he was early there! If he could only be there first, and catch Bob Cratchit coming late! That was the thing he had set his heart upon.

---

blithe: happy and carefree

And he did it. The clock struck nine. No Bob. A quarter past. No Bob. Bob was a full eighteen and a half minutes behind his time. Scrooge sat with his door wide open, that he might see him come into the Tank.

Bob's hat was off before he opened the door; his comforter, too. He was on his stool in a jiffy, driving away with his pen, as if he were trying to overtake nine o'clock.

"Hallo!" growled Scrooge in his accustomed voice, as near as he could feign it. "What do you mean by coming here at this time of day?"

"I am very sorry, sir. I *am* behind my time."

"You are? Yes. I think you are. Step this way, if you please."

"It's only once a year, sir. It shall not be repeated. I was making rather merry yesterday, sir."

"Now, I'll tell you what, my friend. I am not going to stand this sort of thing any longer. And therefore," Scrooge continued, leaping from his stool, and giving Bob such a dig in the waistcoat that he staggered back into the Tank again— "and therefore, I am about to raise your salary!"

Bob trembled, and got a little nearer to the ruler. He had a momentary idea of knocking Scrooge down with it, holding him, and calling to the people in the court for help.

"A Merry Christmas, Bob!" said Scrooge, with an earnestness that could not be mistaken, as he clapped him on the back. "A merrier Christmas, Bob, my good fellow, than I have given you for many a year! I'll raise your salary, and endeavor to assist your struggling family, and we will discuss your affairs this very afternoon, Bob! Make up the fires, and buy a second coal-scuttle before you dot another *i*, Bob Cratchit!"

---

feign: to pretend
coal-scuttle: a bucket for carrying coal

Scrooge was better than his word. He did it all, and infinitely more; and to Tiny Tim, who did NOT die, he was a second father. He became as good a friend, as good a master, and as good a man as the good old city knew, or any other good old city, town, or borough in the good old world. Some people laughed to see the alteration in him; but his own heart laughed, and that was quite enough for him.

He had no further communication with spirits; but it was always said of him that he knew how to keep Christmas well, if any man alive possessed the knowledge. May that be truly said of us, and all of us! And so, as Tiny Tim observed, "God bless us, every one!"

# THE BOY OF THE LONDON STREETS
## A STORY OF YOUNG CHARLES DICKENS
### by Rupert Sargent Holland

The little fellow who worked all day long in the tumble-down old house by the river Thames, pasting oil-paper covers on boxes of blacking, fell ill one afternoon. One of the workmen, a big man named Bob Fagin, made him lie down on a pile of straw in the corner and placed blacking-bottles filled with hot water beside him to keep him warm. There he lay until it was time for the men to stop work, and then Fagin, looking down upon the small boy of twelve, asked if he felt able to go home. The boy got up looking so big-eyed, white-cheeked, and thin, that the man, who had not always been kind before, was moved to put his arm about his shoulder.

"Never mind, Bob, I think I'm all right now," said the boy. "Don't you wait for me; go on home."

"You ain't fit to go alone, Charley. I'm comin' along with you."

"'Deed I am, Bob. I'm feelin' as spry as a cricket." The little fellow threw back his shoulders and headed for the stairs.

Fagin, however, insisted on keeping him company; and so the two, the shabbily-dressed undersized youth and the big heavy man, came out into the murky London twilight and took their way over the Blackfriars Bridge.

---

blacking: a paste used to make things, such as shoes or boots, black
spry: active, lively
murky: cloudy and dark

"Been spendin' your money at the pastry shops, Charley, again? That's what was the matter with you, I take it."

The boy shook his head. "No, Bob. I'm trying to save. When I get my week's money, I put it away in a bureau drawer, wrapped in six little paper packages with a day of the week on each one. Then I know just how much I've got to live on, and Sundays don't count. Sometimes I do get hungry, though; so hungry! Then I look in at the windows and play at being rich."

They crossed the bridge, the boy's big eyes seeming to take note of everything, the man, duller-witted, listening to his chatter. Several times the boy tried to say good-night, but Fagin would not be shaken off. "I'm goin' to see you to your door, Charley lad," he said each time.

At last they came into a little street near the Southwark Bridge. The boy stopped by the steps of a house. "Here 'tis, Bob. Goodnight. It was good of you to take the trouble for me."

"Good-night, Charley."

The boy ran up the steps, and, as he noticed that Fagin still stopped, he pulled the doorbell. Then the man went on down the street. When the door opened the boy asked if Mr. Fagin lived there, and being told that he did not, said he must have made a mistake in the house. Turning about he saw that his friend had disappeared around a corner. With a little smile of triumph he made off in the other direction.

The door of the Marshalsea Prison stood open like a great black mouth. The boy, tired after his long tramp, was glad to reach it and to run in. Climbing several long flights of stairs,

tramp: a long walk

he entered a room on the top story where he found his family: his father, a tall pompous-looking man dressed all in black; his mother, an amiable but extremely fragile woman; and a small brother and sister seated at a table, eating supper. The room was very sparsely furnished; the only bright spot in it was a small fire in a rusty grate, flanked by two bricks to prevent burning too much fuel.

There was a vacant place at the table for Charles, and he sat down upon a stool and ate as ravenously as though he had not tasted food for months. Meanwhile the tall man at the head of the table talked solemnly to his wife at the other end, using strange long words which none of the children could understand.

Supper over, Mr. and Mrs. Dickens (for that was their name) and the two younger children sat before the tiny fire, and Mr. Dickens talked of how he might raise enough money to pay his debts, leave the prison, and start fresh in some new business. Charles had heard these same plans from his father's lips a thousand times before, and so he took from the cupboard an old book which he had bought at a little second-hand shop a few days before, a small tattered copy of *Don Quixote*, and read it by the light of a tallow candle in the corner.

---

pompous: full of self-importance
amiable: friendly
sparsely: minimally; with only a little amount
flanked: placed on both sides of
vacant: empty
ravenously: with extreme hunger
solemnly: very seriously
tattered: worn out; ragged
tallow: substance made of the fat of sheep and cattle

The lines soon blurred before the boy's tired eyes, his head nodded, and he was fast asleep. He was awakened by his father's deep voice. "Time to be leaving, Charles, my son. You have not forgotten that my pecuniary situation prevents my choosing the hour at which I shall close the door of my house. Fortunately it is a predicament which I trust will soon be obviated to our mutual satisfaction."

The small fellow stood up, shook hands solemnly with his father, kissed his mother, and took his way out of the great prison. Open doors on various landings gave him pictures of many peculiar households; sometimes he would stop as though to consider some unusually puzzling face or figure.

Into the night again he went, and wound through a dismal labyrinth of the dark and narrow streets of old London. Sometimes a rough voice or an evil face would frighten him, and he would take to his heels and run as fast as he could. When he passed the house where he had asked for Mr. Fagin, he chuckled to himself; he would not have had his friend know for worlds that his family's home was the Marshalsea Prison.

Even that room in the prison, however, was more cheerful than the small back-attic chamber where the boy fell asleep for the second time that night. He slept on a bed made up on the floor, but his slumber was no less deep on that account.

---

pecuniary: having to do with money
predicament: a difficult situation
obviated: removed; eliminated
mutual: on both sides; shared
peculiar: odd; unusual; strange
dismal: dreary
labyrinth: a maze; interconnecting and often confusing paths
chamber: a room

The noise of workmen in a timber-yard under his window woke Charles when it seemed much too dark to be morning. It was, however, and he was quickly dressed, and making his breakfast from the penny cottage loaf of bread, a section of cream cheese, and small bottle of milk, which were all he could afford to buy from the man who rented him the room. Then he took the roll of paper marked with the name of the day from the drawer of his bureau and counted out the pennies into his pocket. They were not many; he had to live on seven shillings a week, and he tucked them away very carefully in a pocket lest he lose them and have to do without his lunch.

He was not yet due at the blacking factory, but he hurried away from his room and joined the crowd of early morning people already on their way to work. He went down the embankment along the Thames until he came to a place where a bench was set in a corner of a wall. This was his favorite lounging-place; London Bridge was just beyond, the river lay in front of him, and he was far enough away from people to be secure from interruption. As he sat there watching the bridge and the Thames, a small girl came to join him. She was no bigger than he, perhaps a year or two older, but her face was already that of a grown-up woman. She was the maid-of-all-work at a house in the neighborhood, and she had fallen into the habit of stopping to talk for a few moments with the boy on her way to work in the morning. She liked to listen to his stories. This was his hour for inventing them. He could spin wonderful tales about London Bridge, the Tower, and the wharves along the river.

---

embankment: a hill or natural wall
lounging: relaxing; resting

Sometimes he made up stories about the people who passed in front of them, and they were such astonishing stories that the girl remembered them all day as she worked in the house. He seemed to believe them himself; his eyes would grow faraway and dreamy and his words would run on and on until a neighboring clock brought him suddenly back to his own position.

"You do know a heap o' things, don't you?" said the little girl, lost in admiration. "I'd rather have a shillin', though, than all the fairy tales in the world."

"I wouldn't," said Charles, stoutly. "I'd rather read books than do anything else."

"You've got to eat, though," objected his companion; "and books won't make you food. 'T ain't common sense." She relented in an instant. "It's fun though, Charley Dickens. Good-bye till tomorrow."

Charles went on down to the old blacking factory by Hungerford Stairs, a ramshackle building almost hanging over the river, damp and overrun with rats. His place was in a recess of the counting-room on the first floor, and as he covered the bottles with the oil-paper tops and tied them on with a string, he could look from time to time through a window at the slow coal barges swinging down the river.

There were very few boys about the place. At lunchtime he would wander off by himself, and, selecting his meal from a careful survey of several pastry cook's windows, invest his money for the day in fancy cakes or a tart. He missed the company of friends of his own age. Even Fanny,

stoutly: boldly; with determination
relented: gave in
ramshackle: rickety; badly made; unstable
recess: a section of a room set off from the main part

his oldest sister, he only saw on Sundays, when she came back to the Marshalsea from the place where she worked to spend the day with her family. It was only grown-up people that he saw most of the time, and they were too busy with their own affairs to take much interest in the small shabby boy who looked just like any one of a thousand other children

*Dickens as a young man*

of the streets. In all the men at the factory it was only the big clumsy fellow named Fagin who would stop to chat with the lad. So it was that Charles was forced to make friends with whomever he could, people of any age or condition, and was driven to spend much of his spare time roaming about the streets, lounging by the river, reading stray books by a candle in the prison or in the little attic where he slept. It was not a boyhood that seemed to promise much.

In time the boy left the factory and tried being a lawyer's clerk, then a reporter, and at last wrote a book of his own. The book was *The Pickwick Papers,* and it was so original that people clamored for more. Then the young man took note of

clamored: noisily requested

all the strange types of people among whom he had lived as a boy, and those days of poverty and drudgery were turned to wonderful account because he could write of such people and such scenes as he remembered them. The little maid-of-all-work became the "Marchioness" in *The Old Curiosity Shop*, Bob Fagin loaned his name to *Oliver Twist*, and in *David Copperfield* we read the story of the small boy who had to fight his way through London alone. Those days of his boyhood had given him a deep insight into human nature, into the humor and pathos of other people's lives, and it was that rare insight that enabled him to become in time one of the greatest of all English writers.

---

drudgery: unpleasant, dull work
insight: understanding; knowledge
pathos: that which awakens tender feelings, such as pity or sorrow

# LIFE STORIES

# HOMESICK
*by Jean Fritz*

In my father's study there was a large globe with all the countries of the world running around it. I could put my finger on the exact spot where I was and had been ever since I'd been born. And I was on the wrong side of the globe. I was in China in a city named Hankow, a dot on a crooked line that seemed to break the country right in two. The line was really the Yangtse River, but who would know by looking at a map what the Yangtse River really was?

Orange-brown, muddy mustard-colored. And wide, wide, wide. With a river smell that was old and came all the way up from the bottom. Sometimes old women knelt on the riverbank, begging the River God to return a son or grandson who may have drowned. They would wail and beat the earth to make the River God pay attention, but I knew how busy the River God must be. All those people on the Yangtse River! Coolies hauling water. Women washing clothes. Houseboats swarming with old people and young, chickens and pigs. Big crooked-sailed junks with eyes painted on their prows so they could see where they were going. I loved the Yangtse River, but, of course, I belonged on the other side of the world. In America with my grandmother.

---

Yangtse River: (more commonly spelled *Yangtze,* and also called *Chang Jiang*) a very long river (more than 3,400 miles) flowing across central China and into the East China Sea
coolies: unskilled laborers who do low-paying jobs
junks: large, flat-bottomed ships with four-sided sails
prows: fronts of ships

*Twenty-five fluffy little yellow chicks hatched from our eggs today, my grandmother wrote.*

*I wrote my grandmother that I had watched a Chinese magician swallow three yards of fire.*

The trouble with living on the wrong side of the world was that I didn't feel like a real American.

For instance. I could never be president of the United States. I didn't want to be president; I wanted to be a writer. Still, why should there be a law saying that only a person born in the United States could be president? It was as if I wouldn't be American enough.

Actually, I was American every minute of the day, especially during school hours. I went to a British school and every morning we sang "God Save the King." Of course the British children loved singing about their gracious king. Ian Forbes stuck out his chest and sang as if he were saving the king all by himself. Everyone sang. Even Gina Boss who was Italian. And Vera Sebastian who was so Russian she dressed the way Russian girls did long ago before the Revolution when her family had to run away to keep from being killed.

But I wasn't Vera Sebastian. I asked my mother to write an excuse so I wouldn't have to sing, but she wouldn't do it. "When in Rome," she said, "do as the Romans do." What she meant was, "Don't make trouble. Just sing." So for a long time I did. I sang with my fingers crossed but still I felt like a traitor.

Then one day I thought: If my mother and father were really truly in Rome, they wouldn't do what the Romans did at all. They'd probably try to get the Romans to do what *they* did, just as they were trying to teach the Chinese to do

gracious: kind; merciful

what Americans did. (My mother even gave classes in American manners.)

So that day I quit singing. I kept my mouth locked tight against the king of England. Our teacher, Miss Williams, didn't notice at first. She stood in front of the room, using a ruler for a baton, striking each syllable so hard it was as if she were making up for the times she had nothing to strike.

(Miss Williams was pinch-faced and bossy. Sometimes I wondered what had ever made her come to China. "Maybe to try and catch a husband," my mother said.

A husband! Miss Williams!)

"Make him vic-tor-i-ous," the class sang. It was on the strike of "vic" that Miss Williams noticed. Her eyes lighted on my mouth and when we sat down, she pointed her ruler at me.

"Is there something wrong with your voice today, Jean?" she asked.

"No, Miss Williams."

"You weren't singing."

"No, Miss Williams. It is not my national anthem."

"It is the national anthem we sing here," she snapped. "You have always sung. Even Vera sings it."

I looked at Vera with the big blue bow tied on the top of her head. Usually I felt sorry for her but not today. At recess I might even untie that bow, I thought. Just give it a yank. But if I'd been smart, I wouldn't have been looking at Vera. I would have been looking at Ian Forbes and I would have known that, no matter what Miss Williams said, I wasn't through with the king of England.

Recess at the British School was nothing I looked forward to. Every day we played a game called prisoner's base, which was all running and shouting and shoving and catching. I hated the game, yet everyone played except Vera Sebastian. She sat on the sidelines under her blue bow like someone who had been dropped out of a history book. By recess I had forgotten my plans for that bow. While everyone was getting ready for the game, I was as usual trying to look as if I didn't care if I was the last one picked for a team or not. I was leaning against the high stone wall that ran around the schoolyard. I was looking up at a white cloud skittering across the sky when all at once someone tramped down hard on my right foot. Ian Forbes. Snarling bulldog face. Heel grinding down on my toes. Head thrust forward the way an animal might before it strikes.

"You wouldn't sing it. So say it," he ordered. "Let me hear you say it."

I tried to pull my foot away but he only ground down harder.

"Say what?" I was telling my face please not to show what my foot felt.

"*God save the king.* Say it. Those four words. I want to hear you say it."

Although Ian Forbes was short, he was solid and tough and built for fighting. What was more, he always won. You only had to look at his bare knees between the top of his socks and his short pants to know that he would win. His knees were square. Bony and unbeatable. So of course it was crazy for me to argue with him.

"Why should I?" I asked. "Americans haven't said that since George the Third."

He grabbed my right arm and twisted it behind my back.

"Say it," he hissed.

---

sidelines: a place outside of or away from the action

I felt the tears come to my eyes and I hated myself for the tears. I hated myself for not staying in Rome the way my mother had told me.

"I'll never say it," I whispered.

They were choosing sides now in the schoolyard and Ian's name was being called—among the first as always.

He gave my arm another twist. "You'll sing tomorrow," he snarled, "or you'll be bloody sorry."

As he ran off, I slid to the ground, my head between my knees.

*Oh, Grandma, I thought, why can't I be there with you? I'd feed the chickens for you. I'd pump water from the well, the way my father used to do.*

It would be almost two years before we'd go to America. I was ten years old now; I'd be twelve then. But how could I think about years? I didn't even dare to think about the next day. After school I ran all the way home, fast so I couldn't think at all.

Our house stood behind a high stone wall which had chips of broken glass sticking up from the top to keep thieves away. I flung open the iron gate and threw myself through the front door.

"I'm home!" I yelled.

Then I remembered it was Tuesday, the day my mother taught an English class at the Y.M.C.A. where my father was the director.

I stood in the hall, trying to catch my breath, and as always I began to feel small. It was a huge hall with ceilings so high it was as if they would have nothing to do with people. Certainly not with a mere child, not with me—the only child in the house. Once I asked my best friend, Andrea,

Y.M.C.A.: Young Men's Christian Association

if the hall made her feel little too. She said no. She was going to be a dancer and she loved space. She did a high kick to show how grand it was to have room.

Andrea Hull was a year older than I was and knew about everything sooner. She told me about commas, for instance, long before I took punctuation seriously. How could I write letters without commas? she asked. She made me so ashamed that for months I hung little wagging comma-tails all over the letters to my grandmother. She told me things that sounded so crazy I had to ask my mother if they were true. Like where babies come from. And that some day the whole world would end. My mother would frown when I asked her, but she always agreed that Andrea was right. It made me furious. How could she know such things and not tell me? What was the matter with grown-ups anyway?

I wished Andrea were with me now, but she lived out in the country and I didn't see her often. Lin Nai-Nai, my amah, was the only one around, and of course I knew she'd be there. It was her job to stay with me when my parents were out. As soon as she heard me come in, she'd called, "Tsai loushang" which meant that she was upstairs. She might be mending or ironing but most likely she'd be sitting by the window embroidering. And she was. She even had my embroidery laid out, for we had made a bargain. She would teach me to embroider if I would teach her English. I liked embroidering: the cloth stretched tight within my embroidery hoop while I filled in the stamped pattern with cross-stitches and lazy daisy flowers. The trouble was that lazy daisies needed French knots for their centers and I hated making French knots. Mine always fell apart, so I left them to the end. Today I had twenty lazy daisies waiting for their knots.

amah: a nurse or nanny

Lin Nai-Nai had already threaded my needle with embroidery floss.

"Black centers," she said, "for the yellow flowers."

I felt myself glowering. "American flowers don't have centers," I said and gave her back the needle.

Lin Nai-Nai looked at me, puzzled, but she did not argue. She was different from other amahs. She did not even come from the servant class, although this was a secret we had to keep from the other servants who would have made her life miserable, had they known. She had run away from her husband when he had taken a second wife. She would always have been Wife Number One and the Boss no matter how many wives he had, but she would rather be no wife than head of a string of wives. She was modern. She might look old-fashioned, for her feet had been bound up tight when she was a little girl so they would stay small, and now, like many Chinese women, she walked around on little stumps stuffed into tiny cloth shoes. Lin Nai-Nai's were embroidered with butterflies. Still, she believed in true love and one wife for one husband. We were good friends, Lin Nai-Nai and I, so I didn't know why I felt so mean.

She shrugged. "English lesson?" she asked, smiling.

I tested my arm to see if it still hurt from the twist. It did. My foot too. "What do you want to know?" I asked.

We had been through polite phrases—Please, Thank you, I beg your pardon, Excuse me, You're welcome, Merry Christmas (which she had practiced but hadn't had a chance to use since this was only October).

"If I meet an American on the street," she asked, "how do I greet him?"

---

glowering: staring in an angry way; scowling

I looked her straight in the eye and nodded my head in greeting. "Sewing machine," I said. "You say 'Sew-ing ma-chine.'"

She repeated after me, making the four syllables into four separate words. She got up and walked across the room, bowing and smiling. "Sew Ing Ma Shing."

Part of me wanted to laugh at the thought of Lin Nai-Nai maybe meeting Dr. Carhart, our minister, whose face would surely puff up, the way it always did when he was flustered. But part of me didn't want to laugh at all. I didn't like it when my feelings got tangled, so I ran downstairs and played chopsticks on the piano. Loud and fast. When my sore arm hurt, I just beat on the keys harder.

Then I went out to the kitchen to see if Yang Sze-Fu, the cook, would give me something to eat. I found him reading a Chinese newspaper, his eyes going up and down with the characters. (Chinese words don't march across flat surfaces the way ours do; they drop down cliffs, one cliff after another from right to left across a page.)

"Can I have a piece of cinnamon toast?" I asked. "And a cup of cocoa?"

Yang Sze-Fu grunted. He was smoking a cigarette, which he wasn't supposed to do in the kitchen, but Yang Sze-Fu did mostly what he wanted. He considered himself superior to common workers. You could tell because of the fingernails on his pinkies. They were at least two inches long, which was his way of showing that he didn't have to use his hands for rough or dirty work. He didn't seem to care that his fingernails were dirty, but maybe he couldn't keep such long nails clean.

---

flustered: upset due to being confused

He made my toast while his cigarette dangled out of the corner of his mouth, collecting a long ash that finally fell on the floor. He wouldn't have kept smoking if my mother had been there, although he didn't always pay attention to my mother. Never about butter pagodas, for instance. No matter how many times my mother told him before a dinner party, "No butter pagoda," it made no difference. As soon as everyone was seated, the serving boy, Wong Sze-Fu, would bring in a pagoda and set it on the table. The guests would "oh" and "ah," for it was a masterpiece: a pagoda molded out of butter, curved roofs rising tier upon tier, but my mother could only think how unsanitary it was. For, of course, Yang Sze-Fu had molded the butter with his hands and carved the decorations with one of his long fingernails. Still, we always used the butter, for if my mother sent it back to the kitchen, Yang Sze-Fu would lose face and quit.

When my toast and cocoa were ready, I took them upstairs to my room (the blue room) and while I ate, I began *Sara Crewe* again. Now there was a girl, I thought, who was worth crying over. I wasn't going to think about myself. Or Ian Forbes. Or the next day. I wasn't. I wasn't.

And I didn't. Not all afternoon. Not all evening. Still, I must have decided what I was going to do because the next morning when I started for school and came to the corner where the man sold hot chestnuts, the corner where I always turned to go to school, I didn't turn. I walked straight ahead. I wasn't going to school that day.

I walked toward the Yangtse River. Past the store that sold paper pellets that opened up into flowers when you dropped them in a glass of water. Then up the block where the

pagodas: in Asia, tower-like temples
lose face: be disgraced or dishonored

beggars sat. I never saw anyone give money to a beggar. You couldn't, my father explained, or you'd be mobbed by beggars. They'd follow you everyplace; they'd never leave you alone. I had learned not to look at them when I passed and yet I saw. The running sores, the twisted legs, the mangled faces. What I couldn't get over was that, like me, each one of those beggars had one life to live. It just happened that they had drawn rotten ones.

*Oh, Grandma, I thought, we may be far apart but we're lucky, you and I. Do you even know how lucky? In America do you know?*

This part of the city didn't actually belong to the Chinese, even though the beggars sat there, even though the upper-class Chinese lived there. A long time ago other countries had just walked into China and divided up part of Hankow (and other cities) into sections, or concessions, which they called their own and used their own rules for governing. We lived in the French concession on Rue de Paris. Then there was the British concession and the Japanese. The Russian and German concessions had been officially returned to China, but the people still called them concessions. The Americans didn't have one, although, like some of the other countries, they had gunboats on the river. In case, my father said. In case what? Just in case. That's all he'd say.

The concessions didn't look like the rest of China. The buildings were solemn and orderly with little plots of grass around them. Not like those in the Chinese part of the city: a jumble of rickety shops with people, vegetables, crates of quacking ducks, yard goods, bamboo baskets, and mangy dogs spilling onto a street so narrow it was hardly there.

---

Rue de Paris: French for "Street of Paris"
solemn: serious; gloomy

The grandest street in Hankow was the Bund, which ran along beside the Yangtse River. When I came to it after passing the beggars, I looked to my left and saw the American flag flying over the American consulate building. I was proud of the flag and I thought maybe it was proud of me. It flapped in the breeze as if it were saying ha-ha to the king of England.

Then I looked to the right at the Customs House, which stood at the other end of the Bund. The clock on top of the tower said nine-thirty. How would I spend the day?

I crossed the street to the promenade part of the Bund. When people walked here, they weren't usually going anyplace; they were just out for the air. My mother would wear her broad-brimmed beaver hat when we came and my father would swing his cane in that jaunty way that showed how glad he was to be a man. I thought I would just sit on a bench for the morning. I would watch the Customs House clock, and when it was time, I would eat the lunch I had brought along in my schoolbag.

I was the only one sitting on a bench. People did not generally "take the air" on a Wednesday morning and besides, not everyone was allowed here. The British had put a sign on the Bund, NO DOGS, NO CHINESE. This meant that I could never bring Lin Nai-Nai with me. My father couldn't even bring his best friend, Mr. T.K. Hu. Maybe the British wanted a place where they could pretend they weren't in China, I

---

consulate: the home or office of a government's representative in a
    foreign city
Customs House: the office in which government officials inspect imported
    and exported goods and collect taxes ("customs") on them
promenade: a public space meant for walking
jaunty: lively; upbeat

thought. Still, there were always Chinese coolies around. In order to load and unload boats in the river, coolies had to cross the Bund. All day they went back and forth, bent double under their loads, sweating and chanting in a tired singsong way that seemed to get them from one step to the next.

To pass the time, I decided to recite poetry. The one good thing about Miss Williams was that she made us learn poems by heart and I liked that. There was one particular poem I didn't want to forget. I looked at the Yangtse River and pretended that all the busy people in the boats were my audience.

"'Breathes there the man, with soul so dead,'" I cried, "'Who never to himself hath said, This is my own, my native land!'"

I was so carried away by my performance that I didn't notice the policeman until he was right in front of me. Like all policemen in the British concession, he was a bushy-bearded Indian with a red turban wrapped around his head.

He pointed to my schoolbag. "Little miss," he said, "why aren't you in school?"

He was tall and mysterious-looking, more like a character in my Arabian Nights book than a man you expected to talk to. I fumbled for an answer. "I'm going on an errand," I said finally. "I just sat down for a rest." I picked up my schoolbag and walked quickly away. When I looked around, he was back on his corner, directing traffic.

So now they were chasing children away too, I thought angrily. Well, I'd like to show them. Someday I'd like to walk a dog down the whole length of the Bund. A Great Dane. I'd have him on a leash—like this— (I put out my hand as if I

---

turban: a long scarf wound around one's head

were holding a leash right then) and he'd be so big and strong I'd have to strain to hold him back (I strained). Then of course sometimes he'd have to do his business and I'd stop (like this) right in the middle of the sidewalk and let him go to it. I was so busy with my Great Dane I was at the end of the Bund before I knew it. I let go of the leash, clapped my hands, and told my dog to go home. Then I left the Bund and the concessions and walked into the Chinese world.

My mother and father and I walked here before but not for many months. This part near the river was called the Mud Flats. Sometimes it was muddier than others, and when the river flooded, the flats disappeared underwater. Sometimes even the fishermen's huts were washed away, knocked right off their long-legged stilts and swept down the river. But today the river was fairly low and the mud had dried so that it was cracked and cakey. Most of the men who lived here were out fishing, some not far from the shore, poling their sampans through the shallow water. Only a few people were on the flats: a man cleaning a fish on a flat rock at the water's edge, a woman spreading clothes on the dirt to dry, a few small children. But behind the huts was something I had never seen before. Even before I came close, I guessed what it was. Even then, I was excited by the strangeness of it.

It was the beginnings of a boat. The skeleton of a large junk, its ribs lying bare, its backbone running straight and true down the bottom. The outline of the prow was already in place, turning up wide and snub-nosed, the way all junks did. I had never thought of boats starting from nothing, of taking on bones under their bodies. The eyes, I supposed, would be the last thing added. Then the junk would have life.

---

sampans: small, flat-bottomed boats

The builders were not there and I was behind the huts where no one could see me as I walked around and around, marveling. Then I climbed inside and as I did, I knew that something wonderful was happening to me. I was a-tingle, the way a magician must feel when he swallows fire, because suddenly I knew the boat was mine. No matter who really owned it, it was mine. Even if I never saw it again, it would be my junk sailing up and down the Yangtse River. My junk seeing the river sights with its two eyes, seeing them for me whether I was there or not. Often I had tried to put the Yangtse River into a poem so I could keep it. Sometimes I had tried to draw it, but nothing I did ever came close. But now, now I had my junk and somehow that gave me the river too.

I thought I should put my mark on the boat. Perhaps on the side of the spine. Very small. A secret between the boat and me. I opened my schoolbag and took out my folding penknife that I used for sharpening pencils. Very carefully I carved the Chinese character that was our name. Gau. (In China my father was Mr. Gau, my mother was Mrs. Gau, and I was Little Miss Gau.) The builders would paint right over the character, I thought, and never notice. But I would know. Always and forever I would know.

For a long time I dreamed about the boat, imagining it finished, its sails up, its eyes wide. Someday, it might sail all the way down the Yangtse to Shanghai, so I told the boat what it would see along the way because I had been there and the boat hadn't. After a while I got hungry and I ate my egg sandwich. I was in the midst of peeling an orange when all at once I had company.

---

marveling: feeling wonder, surprise, and amazement

A small boy, not more than four years old, wandered around to the back of the huts, saw me, and stopped still. He was wearing a ragged blue cotton jacket with a red cloth, pincushion-like charm around his neck which was supposed to keep him from getting smallpox. Sticking up straight from the middle of his head was a small pigtail which I knew was to fool the gods and make them think he was a girl. (Gods didn't bother much with girls; it was the boys that were important in China.) The weather was still warm so he wore no pants, nothing below the waist. Most small boys went around like this so that when they had to go, they could just let loose and go. He walked slowly up to the boat, stared at me, and then nodded as if he'd already guessed what I was. "Foreign devil," he announced gravely.

I shook my heard. "No," I said in Chinese. "American friend." Through the ribs of the boat, I handed him a segment of orange. He ate it slowly, his eyes on the rest of the orange. Segment by segment, I gave it all to him. Then he wiped his hands down the front of his jacket.

"Foreign devil," he repeated.

"American friend," I corrected. Then I asked him about the boat. Who was building it? Where were the builders?

He pointed with his chin upriver. "Not here today. Back tomorrow."

I knew it would only be a question of time before the boy would run off to alert the people in the huts. "Foreign devil, foreign devil," he would cry. So I put my hand on the prow of the boat, wished it luck, and climbing out, I stared back toward the Bund. To my surprise the boy walked beside me.

---

smallpox: a dangerous contagious disease that in past times
  killed thousands

When we came to the edge of the Bund, I squatted down so we would be on the same eye level.

"Good-bye," I said. "May the River God protect you."

For a moment the boy stared. When he spoke, it was as if he were trying out a new sound. "American friend," he said slowly.

When I looked back, he was still there, looking soberly toward the foreign world to which I had gone.

The time, according to the Customs House clock, was five after two, which meant I couldn't go home for two hours. School was dismissed at three-thirty and I was home by three-forty-five unless I had to stay in for talking in class. It took me about fifteen minutes to write "I will not talk in class" fifty times, and so I often came home at four o'clock. (I wrote up and down like the Chinese: fifty "I's," fifty "wills," and right through the sentence so I never had to think what I was writing. It wasn't as if I were making a promise.) Today I planned to arrive home at four, my "staying-in" time, in the hope that I wouldn't meet classmates on the way.

Meanwhile I wandered up and down the streets, in and out of stores. I weighed myself on the big scale in the Hankow Dispensary and found that I was as skinny as ever. I went to the Terminus Hotel and tried out the chairs in the lounge. At first I didn't mind wandering about like this. Half of my mind was still on the river with my junk, but as time went on, my junk began slipping away until I was alone with nothing but questions. Would my mother find out about today? How could I skip school tomorrow? And the next day and the next? Could I get sick? Was there a kind of long lie-abed sickness that didn't hurt?

I arrived home at four, just as I had planned, opened the

dispensary: a medical clinic

door, and called out, "I'm home!" Cheery-like and normal. But I was scarcely in the house before Lin Nai-Nai ran to me from one side of the hall and my mother from the other.

"Are you all right? Are you all right?" Lin Nai-Nai felt my arms as if she expected them to be broken. My mother's face was white. "What happened?" she asked.

Then I looked through the open door into the living room and saw Miss Williams sitting there. She had beaten me home and asked about my absence, which of course had scared everyone. But now my mother could see that I was in one piece and for some reason this seemed to make her mad. She took me by the hand and led me into the living room. "Miss Williams said you weren't in school," she said. "Why was that?"

I hung my head, just the way cowards do in books.

My mother dropped my hand. "Jean will be in school tomorrow," she said firmly. She walked Miss Williams to the door. "Thank you for stopping by."

Miss Williams looked satisfied in her mean, pinched way. "Well," she said, "ta-ta." (She always said "ta-ta" instead of "good-bye." Chicken language, it sounded like.)

As soon as Miss Williams was gone and my mother was sitting down again, I burst into tears. Kneeling on the floor, I buried my head in her lap and poured out the whole miserable story. My mother could see that I really wasn't in one piece after all, so she listened quietly, stroking my hair as I talked, but gradually I could feel her stiffen. I knew she was remembering that she was a Mother.

"You better go up to your room," she said, "and think things over. We'll talk about it after supper."

I flung myself on my bed. What was there to think? Either I went to school and got beaten up. Or I quit. After supper I explained to my mother and father how simple it was. I could stay at home and my mother could teach me, the way Andrea's mother taught her. Maybe I could even go to Andrea's house and study with her.

My mother shook her head. Yes, it was simple, she agreed. I could go back to the British School, be sensible, and start singing about the king again.

I clutched the edge of the table. Couldn't she understand? I couldn't turn back now. It was too late.

So far my father had not said a word. He was leaning back, teetering on the two hind legs of his chair, the way he always did after a meal, the way that drove my mother crazy. But he was not the type of person to keep all four legs on a chair on the floor just because someone wanted him to. He wasn't a turning-back person so I hoped maybe he would understand. As I watched him, I saw a twinkle start in his eyes and suddenly he brought his chair down slam-bang flat on the floor. He got up and motioned for us to follow him into the living room. He sat down at the piano and began to pick out the tune for "God Save the King."

A big help, I thought. Was he going to make me practice? Then he began to sing:

"My country 'tis of thee,
Sweet land of liberty, . . ."

Of course! It was the same tune. Why hadn't I thought of that? Who would know what I was singing as long as I moved my lips? I joined in now, loud and strong.

"Of thee I sing."

My mother laughed in spite of herself. "If you sing that loud," she said, "you'll start a revolution."

"Tomorrow, I'll sing softly," I promised. "No one will know." But for now I really let freedom ring.

Then all at once I wanted to see Lin Nai-Nai. I ran out back, through the courtyard that separated the house from the servants' quarters, and upstairs to her room.

"It's me," I called through the door and when she opened up, I threw my arms around her. "Oh, Lin Nai-Nai, I love you," I said. "You haven't said it yet, have you?"

"Said what?"

"Sewing machine. You haven't said it?"

"No," she said, "not yet. I'm still practicing."

"Don't say it, Lin Nai-Nai. Say 'Good day.' It's shorter and easier. Besides, it's more polite."

"Good day?" she repeated.

"Yes, that's right. Good day." I hugged her and ran back to the house.

The next day at school when we rose to sing the British national anthem, everyone stared at me, but as soon as I opened my mouth, the class lost interest. All but Ian Forbes. His eyes never left my face, but I sang softly, carefully, proudly. At recess he sauntered over to where I stood against the wall.

He spat on the ground. "You can be bloody glad you sang today," he said." Then he strutted off as if he and those square knees of his had won again.

And, of course, I was bloody glad.

---

sauntered: walked casually

# BREATHES THERE THE MAN

*by Sir Walter Scott*

Breathes there the man with soul so dead,
Who never to himself hath said,
   "This is my own, my native land!"
Whose heart hath ne'er within him burn'd,
As home his footsteps he hath turn'd
     From wandering on a foreign strand?

If such there breathe, go, mark him well;
For him no minstrel raptures swell;
High though his titles, proud his name,
Boundless his wealth as wish can claim;
Despite those titles, power, and pelf,
The wretch, concentred all in self,
Living, shall forfeit fair renown,
And, doubly dying, shall go down
To the vile dust, from whence he sprung,
Unwept, unhonored, and unsung.

---

native land: the land where one was born
strand: shore
minstrel: in ancient times, a poet or singer of verses
raptures: expressions of overwhelming joy
swell: to expand with emotion
boundless: without limits; vast
pelf: riches
concentred: concentrated
forfeit: to lose something because of some error or wrongdoing
fair renown: a good reputation
vile: foul; disgusting; worthless

# MAMI AND PAPI

*from* When I Was Puerto Rican
*by Esmeralda Santiago*

**W**e came to Macún when I was four, to a rectangle of ripped metal sheets on stilts hovering in the middle of a circle of red dirt. Our home was a giant version of the lard cans used to haul water from the public fountain. Its windows and doors were also metal, and, as we stepped in, I touched the wall and burned my fingers.

"That'll teach you," Mami scolded. "Never touch a wall on the sunny side."

She searched a bundle of clothes and diapers for her jar of Vick's VapoRub to smear on my fingers. They were red the rest of the day, and I couldn't suck my thumb that night. "You're too big for that anyway," she said.

The floor was a patchwork of odd-shaped wooden slats that rose in the middle and dipped toward the front and back doors, where they butted against shiny, worn thresholds. Papi nailed new boards under Mami's treadle sewing machine, and under their bed, but the floor still groaned and sagged to the corners, threatening to collapse and bring the house down with it.

"I'll rip the whole thing out," Papi suggested. "We'll have to live with a dirt floor for a while…"

Mami looked at her feet and shuddered. A dirt floor, we'd heard, meant snakes and scorpions could crawl into the

---

thresholds: doorsills; planks or stones under a door
treadle: the pedal that operates an old sewing machine

house from their holes in the ground. Mami didn't know any better, and I had yet to learn not everything I heard was true, so we reacted in what was to become a pattern for us: what frightened her I became curious about, and what she found exciting terrified me. As Mami pulled her feet onto the rungs of her rocking chair and rubbed the goose bumps from her arms, I imagined a world of fascinating creatures slithering underfoot, drawing squiggly patterns on the dirt.

The day Papi tore up the floor, I followed him holding a can into which he dropped the straight nails, still usable. My fingers itched with a rust-colored powder, and when I licked them, a dry, metallic taste curled the tip of my tongue. Mami stood on the threshold scratching one ankle with the toes of the other foot.

"Negi, come help me gather kindling for the fire."

"I'm working with Papi," I whined, hoping he'd ask me to stay. He didn't turn around but continued on his knees, digging out nails with the hammer's claw, muttering the words to his favorite chachachá.

"Do as I say!" Mami ordered. Still, Papi kept his back to us. I plunked the can full of nails down hard, willing him to hear and tell me to stay, but he didn't. I dawdled after Mami down the three steps into the yard. Delsa and Norma, my younger sisters, took turns swinging from a rope Papi had hung under the mango tree.

"Why can't they help with the kindling?" I pouted.

Mami swatted the side of my head. "Don't talk back," she said. "You girls keep away from the house while your father is working," she warned as we walked by my sisters having fun.

---

kindling: material used to start a fire, such as dry sticks or leaves
dawdled: moved slowly and aimlessly

She led the way into a thicket behind the latrine. Twigs crackled under my bare feet, stinging the soles. A bananaquit flew to the thorny branch of a lemon tree and looked from side to side. Dots of sun danced on the green walls of the shady grove above low bushes weighted with pigeon peas, the earth screened with twigs, sensitive *morivoví* plants, and french weed studded with tiny blue flowers. Mami hummed softly, the yellow and orange flowers on her dress blending into the greenness: a miraculous garden with legs and arms and a melody. Her hair, choked at the nape with a rubber band, floated thick and black to her waist, and as she bent over to pick up sticks, it rained across her shoulders and down her arms, covering her face and tangling in the twigs she cradled. A red butterfly circled her and flew close to her ear. She gasped and swatted it into a bush.

"It felt like it was going right into my brain," she muttered with an embarrassed smile.

Delsa and Norma toddled through the underbrush. "Mami, come see what I found," Delsa called.

A hen had scratched out a hollow and carpeted its walls and floor with dry grass. She had laid four eggs, smaller and not as white as the ones our neighbor Doña Lola gave us from time to time.

"Can we eat them?" Delsa asked.

"No."

"But if we leave them here a snake will get them," I said, imagining a serpent swallowing each egg whole. Mami

---

latrine: an outdoor, shared bathroom
bananaquit: a small, colorful bird commonly found in warm climates
*morivoví*: a flower common in Puerto Rico and other parts of the Caribbean
miraculous: like a miracle; marvelous
nape: the back of the neck
Doña: in Spanish, a respectful title for a woman

shuddered and rubbed her arms where tiny bumps had formed making the fine hairs stand straight up. She gave me a look, half puzzled, half angry, and drew us to her side.

"All right, let's get our sticks together and bring them to the kitchen." As she picked hers up, she looked carefully around.

"One, two, three, four," she chanted. "One, two, three, four."

We marched single file into our yard, where Papi stacked floorboards.

"Come look," he said.

The dirt was orange, striped in places where crumbs had slipped through the cracks when Mami swept. Papi had left a few boards down the center of the room and around his and Mami's bed, to stand on until the ground was swept and flattened. Mami was afraid to come into the house. There were small holes in the dirt, holes where snakes and scorpions hid. She turned swiftly and threw herself off balance so that she skipped toward the kitchen shed.

"Let's go make supper!" She singsang to make it sound like fun. Delsa and Norma followed her skirt, but I stared at the dirt, where squiggly lines stretched from one wall to the other. Mami waited for me.

"Negi, come help in the kitchen."

I pretended not to hear but felt her eyes bore holes in the back of my head. Papi stepped between us.

"Let her stay. I can use the help."

I peered between his legs and saw her squint and pucker her lips as if she were about to spit. He chuckled, "Heh, heh," and she whirled toward the kitchen shed, where the fire in the *fogón* was almost out.

---

*fogón*: Spanish word meaning "fireplace" or "furnace"

"Take these boards and lay them on the pile for the cooking fire," Papi said. "Careful with the splinters."

I walked a broad circle around Mami, who looked up from her vegetable chopping whenever I went by. When I passed carrying a wide board, Mami asked to see it. Black bugs, like ants, but bigger and blacker, crawled over it in a frenzy.

"Termites!" she gasped.

I was covered with them. They swarmed inside my shirt and panties, into my hair, under my arms. Until Mami saw them, I hadn't felt them sting. But they bit ridges into my skin that itched and hurt at the same time. Mami ran me to the washtub and dunked me among my father's soaking shirts.

"Pablo!" she called, "Oh, my God! Look at her. She's being eaten alive!"

I screamed, imagining my skin disappearing in chunks into the invisible mouths of hundreds of tiny black specks creeping into parts of my body I couldn't even reach. Mami pulled off my clothes and threw them on the ground. The soap in the washtub burned my skin, and Mami scrubbed me so hard her fingernails dug angry furrows into my arms and legs. She turned me around to wash my back, and I almost fell out of the tub.

"Be still," she said. "I have to get them all."

She pushed and shoved and turned me so fast I didn't know what to do with my body, so I flailed, seeming to resist, while in fact I wanted nothing more than to be rid of the creepy crawling things that covered me. Mami wrapped me in a towel and lifted me out of the tub with a groan.

---

frenzy: a state of wild excitement
furrows: grooves, like the tracks left by a plow
flailed: moved as though beating or striking something

Hundreds of black bugs floated between the bubbles.

She carried me to the house pressed against her bosom, fragrant of curdled milk. Delsa and Norma ran after us, but Papi scooped them up, one on each arm, and carried them to the rope swing. Mami balanced on the floorboards to her bed, lay me beside her, held me tight, kissed my forehead, my eyes, and murmured, "It's all right. It's over. It's all right."

I wrapped my legs around her and buried my face under her chin. It felt so good to have Mami so close, so warm, swathed by her softness, her smell of wood smoke and oregano. She rubbed circles on my back and caressed the hair from my face. She kissed me, brushed my tears with her fingertips, and dried my nose with the towel, or the hem of her dress.

"You see," she murmured, "what happens when you don't do what I say?"

I turned away from her and curled into a tight ball of shame. Mami rolled off the bed and went outside. I lay on her pillow, whimpering, wondering how the termites knew I'd disobeyed my mother.

---

swathed: wrapped; covered
oregano: an herb used as a seasoning
caressed: gently stroked or rubbed

# THE NIGHT THE BED FELL
*by James Thurber*

I suppose that the high-water mark of my youth in Columbus, Ohio, was the night the bed fell on my father. It makes a better recitation (unless, as some friends of mine have said, one has heard it five or six times) than it does a piece of writing, for it is almost necessary to throw furniture around, shake doors, and bark like a dog, to lend the proper atmosphere and verisimilitude to what is admittedly a somewhat incredible tale. Still, it did take place.

It happened, then, that my father had decided to sleep in the attic one night, to be away where he could think. My mother opposed the notion strongly because, she said, the old wooden bed up there was unsafe: it was wobbly and the heavy headboard would crash down on father's head in case the bed fell, and kill him. There was no dissuading him, however, and at a quarter past ten he closed the attic door behind him and went up the narrow twisting stairs. We later heard ominous creakings as he crawled into bed. Grandfather, who usually slept in the attic bed when he was with us, had disappeared some days before. (On these occasions he was usually gone six or seven days and returned growling and out of temper, with the news that the Federal Union was run

---

high-water mark: highest point; most notable moment or occurrence
recitation: a spoken presentation
verisimilitude: the appearance of being true
dissuading: persuading not to do something; advising against
ominous: threatening; signaling danger
Federal Union: in the Civil War, the North

by a passel of blockheads and that the Army of the Potomac didn't have a chance.)

We had visiting us at this time a nervous first cousin of mine named Briggs Beall, who believed that he was likely to cease breathing when he was asleep. It was his feeling that if he were not awakened every hour during the night, he might die of suffocation. He had been accustomed to setting an alarm clock to ring at intervals until morning, but I persuaded him to abandon this. He slept in my room and I told him that I was such a light sleeper that if anybody quit breathing in the same room with me, I would wake instantly. He tested me the first night—which I had suspected he would—by holding his breath after my regular breathing had convinced him I was asleep. I was not asleep, however, and called to him. This seemed to allay his fears a little, but he took the precaution of putting a glass of spirits of camphor on a little table at the head of his bed. In case I didn't arouse him until he was almost gone, he said, he would sniff the camphor, a powerful reviver.

Briggs was not the only member of his family who had his crotchets. Old Aunt Melissa Beall (who could whistle like a man, with two fingers in her mouth) suffered under the premonition that she was destined to die on South High Street, because she had been born on South High Street and married on South High Street. Then there was Aunt Sarah

---

passel: a large number of something
Army of the Potomac: one of the Northern armies during the Civil War
allay: to ease; to calm
camphor: a substance with a strong odor, sometimes used for medical purposes
crotchets: odd habits
premonition: a feeling that something (usually bad) is soon to happen

Shoaf, who never went to bed at night without the fear that a burglar was going to get in and blow chloroform under her door through a tube. To avert this calamity—for she was in greater dread of anesthetics than of losing her household goods—she always piled her money, silverware, and other valuables in a neat stack just outside her bedroom, with a note reading,: "This is all I have. Please take it and do not use your chloroform, as this is all I have." Aunt Gracie Shoaf also had a burglar phobia, but she met it with more fortitude. She was confident that burglars had been getting into her house every night for four years. The fact that she never missed anything was to her no proof to the contrary. She always claimed that she scared them off before they could take anything, by throwing shoes down the hallway. When she went to bed she piled, where she could get at them handily, all the shoes there were about her house. Five minutes after she had turned off the light, she would sit up in bed and say "Hark!" Her husband, who had learned to ignore the whole situation as long ago as 1903, would either be sound asleep or pretend to be sound asleep. In either case he would not respond to her tugging and pulling, so that presently she would arise, tiptoe to the door, open it slightly and heave a shoe down the hall in one direction, and its mate down the hall in the other direction. Some nights she threw them all, some nights only a couple of pair.

But I am straying from the remarkable incidents that took place during the night that the bed fell on father. By midnight

chloroform: a substance that can render people unconscious, once
    frequently used as an anesthetic
calamity: disaster; catastrophe
anesthetics: substances used to take away feeling, sometimes by rendering
    a person unconscious
fortitude: strength and determination in the face of challenges

we were all in bed. The layout of the rooms and the disposition of their occupants is important to an understanding of what later occurred. In the front room upstairs (just under father's attic bedroom) were my mother and my brother Terry, who sometimes sang in his sleep, usually "Marching Through

Georgia" or "Onward, Christian Soldiers." Briggs Beall and myself were in a room adjoining this one. My brother Roy was in a room across the hall from ours. Our bull terrier, Rex, slept in the hall.

My bed was an army cot, one of those affairs which are made wide enough to sleep on comfortably only by putting up, flat with the middle section, the two sides which ordinarily hang down like the sideboards of a drop-leaf table. When these sides are up, it is perilous to roll too far toward the edge, for then the cot is likely to tip completely over, bringing the whole bed down on top of one, with a tremendous banging crash. This, in fact, is precisely what happened, about two o'clock in the morning. (It was my mother who, in recalling the scene later, first referred to it as "the night the bed fell on your father.")

---

disposition: arrangement; placement
perilous: dangerous

Always a deep sleeper, slow to arouse (I had lied to Briggs), I was at first unconscious of what had happened when the iron cot rolled me onto the floor and toppled over on me. It left me still warmly bundled up and unhurt, for the bed rested above me like a canopy. Hence I did not wake up, only reached the edge of consciousness and went back. The racket, however, instantly awakened my mother, in the next room, who came to the immediate conclusion that her worst dread was realized: the big wooden bed upstairs had fallen on father. She therefore screamed, "Let's go to your poor father!" It was this shout, rather than the noise of my cot falling, that awakened Herman, in the same room with her. He thought that mother had become, for no apparent reason, hysterical. "You're all right, Mamma!" he shouted, trying, to calm her. They exchanged shout for shout for perhaps ten seconds: "Let's go to your poor father!" and "You're all right!" That woke up Briggs. By this time I was conscious of what was going on, in a vague way, but did not yet realize that I was under my bed instead of on it. Briggs, awakening in the midst of loud shouts of fear and apprehension, came to the quick conclusion that he was suffocating and that we were all trying to "bring him out." With a low moan, he grasped the glass of camphor at the head of his bed and instead of sniffing it poured it over himself. The room reeked of camphor. "Ugf, ahfg," choked Briggs, like a drowning man, for he had almost succeeded in stopping his breathing under the deluge of pungent spirits. He leaped out of bed and groped toward the open window, but he came up against one that was closed. With his hand, he beat out the glass, and I could hear it crash and tinkle on the alleyway

deluge: a flood
pungent: having a sharp, stinging smell

below. It was at this juncture that I, in trying to get up, had the uncanny sensation of feeling my bed above me! Foggy with sleep, I now suspected, in my turn, that the whole uproar was being made in a frantic endeavor to extricate me from what must be an unheard-of and perilous situation. "Get me out of this!" I bawled. "Get me out!" I think I had the nightmarish belief that I was entombed in a mine. "Gugh," gasped Briggs, floundering in his camphor.

By this time my mother, still shouting, pursued by Herman, still shouting, was trying to open the door to the attic, in order to go up and get my father's body out of the wreckage. The door was stuck, however, and wouldn't yield. Her frantic pulls on it only added to the general banging and confusion. Roy and the dog were now up, the one shouting questions, the other barking.

Father, farthest away and soundest sleeper of all, had by this time been awakened by the battering on the attic door. He decided that the house was on fire. "I'm coming, I'm coming!" he wailed in a slow, sleepy voice—it took him many minutes to regain full consciousness. My mother, still believing he was caught under the bed, detected in his "I'm coming!" the mournful, resigned note of one who is preparing to meet his Maker. "He's dying!" she shouted.

"I'm all right!" Briggs yelled to reassure her. "I'm all right!" He still believed that it was his own closeness to death that was worrying mother. I found at last the light

juncture: a point in time at which events come together in some
    significant way
uncanny: weird; eerie; mysterious
frantic: wildly anxious; panicky
endeavor: an effort; an attempt
extricate: to free from a difficult position or situation
floundering: moving clumsily

switch in my room, unlocked the door, and Briggs and I joined the others at the attic door. The dog, who never did like Briggs, jumped for him—assuming that he was the culprit in whatever was going on—and Roy had to throw Rex and hold him. We could hear father crawling out of bed upstairs. Roy pulled the attic door open with a mighty jerk, and father came down the stairs, sleepy and irritable but safe and sound. My mother began to weep when she saw him. Rex began to howl. "What in the name of God is going on here?" asked father.

The situation was finally put together like a gigantic jigsaw puzzle. Father caught a cold from prowling around in his bare feet but there were no other bad results. "I'm glad," said mother, who always looked on the bright side of things, "that your grandfather wasn't here."

---

culprit: a guilty person

# WHAT'S IMPORTANT

# PRESIDENT CLEVELAND, WHERE ARE YOU?

*by Robert Cormier*

That was the autumn of the cowboy cards—Buck Jones and Tom Tyler and Hoot Gibson and especially Ken Maynard. The cards were available in those five-cent packages of gum: pink sticks, three together, covered with a sweet white powder. You couldn't blow bubbles with that particular gum, but it couldn't have mattered less. The cowboy cards were important—the pictures of those rock-faced men with eyes of blue steel.

On those windswept, leaf-tumbling afternoons we gathered after school on the sidewalk in front of Lemire's Drugstore, across from St. Jude's Parochial School, and we swapped and bargained and matched for the cards. Because a Ken Maynard serial was playing at the Globe every Saturday afternoon, he was the most popular cowboy of all, and one of his cards was worth at least ten of any other kind. Rollie Tremaine had a treasure of thirty or so, and he guarded them jealously. He'd match you for the other cards, but he risked his Ken Maynards only when the other kids threatened to leave him out of the competition altogether.

You could almost hate Rollie Tremaine. In the first place, he was the only son of Auguste Tremaine, who operated the Uptown Dry Goods Store, and he did not live in a tenement but in a big white birthday cake of a house on Laurel Street.

---

parochial school: a school run by a religious group
serial: a movie shown in episodes over time
tenement: an apartment building, often run-down

He was too fat to be effective in the football games between the Frenchtown Tigers and the North Side Knights, and he made us constantly aware of the jingle of coins in his pockets. He was able to stroll into Lemire's and casually select a quarter's worth of cowboy cards while the rest of us watched, aching with envy.

Once in a while I earned a nickel or dime by running errands or washing windows for blind old Mrs. Belander, or by finding pieces of copper, brass, and other valuable metals at the dump and selling them to the junkman. The coins clutched in my hand, I would race to Lemire's to buy a cowboy card or two, hoping that Ken Maynard would stare boldly out at me as I opened the pack. At one time, before a disastrous matching session with Roger Lussier (my best friend, except where the cards were involved), I owned five Ken Maynards and considered myself a millionaire, of sorts.

One week I was particularly lucky; I had spent two afternoons washing floors for Mrs. Belander and received a quarter. Because my father had worked a full week at the shop, where a rush order for fancy combs had been received, he allotted my brothers and sisters and me an extra dime along with the usual ten cents for the Saturday-afternoon movie. Setting aside the movie fare, I found myself with a bonus of thirty-five cents, and I then planned to put Rollie Tremaine to shame the following Monday afternoon.

Monday was the best day to buy the cards because the candy man stopped at Lemire's every Monday morning to deliver the new assortments. There was nothing more

---

allotted: gave
assortments: collections of various things

exciting in the world than a fresh batch of card boxes. I rushed home from school that day and hurriedly changed my clothes, eager to set off for the store. As I burst through the doorway, letting the screen door slam behind me, my brother Armand blocked my way.

He was fourteen, three years older than I, and a freshman at Monument High School. He had recently become a stranger to me in many ways—indifferent to such matters as cowboy cards and the Frenchtown Tigers—and he carried himself with a mysterious dignity that was fractured now and then when his voice began shooting off in all directions like some kind of vocal fireworks.

"Wait a minute, Jerry," he said. "I want to talk to you." He motioned me out of earshot of my mother, who was busy supervising the usual after-school skirmish in the kitchen.

I sighed with impatience. In recent months Armand had become a figure of authority, siding with my father and mother occasionally. As the oldest son he sometimes took advantage of his age and experience to issue rules and regulations.

"How much money have you got?" he whispered.

"You in some kind of trouble?" I asked, excitement rising in me as I remembered the blackmail plot of a movie at the Globe a month before.

He shook his head in annoyance. "Look," he said, "it's Pa's birthday tomorrow. I think we ought to chip in and buy him something…"

---

indifferent to: uninterested in
dignity: a quality of character that commands honor and respect
fractured: broken
skirmish: a minor conflict or fight

I reached into my pocket and caressed the coins. "Here," I said carefully, pulling out a nickel. "If we all give a nickel we should have enough to buy him something pretty nice."

He regarded me with contempt. "Rita already gave me fifteen cents, and I'm throwing in a quarter. Albert handed over a dime—all that's left of his birthday money. Is that all you can do—a nickel?"

"Aw, come on," I protested. "I haven't got a single Ken Maynard left, and I was going to buy some cards this afternoon."

"Ken Maynard!" he snorted. "Who's more important—him or your father?"

His question was unfair because he knew that there was no possible choice—"my father" had to be the only answer. My father was a huge man who believed in the things of the spirit, although my mother often maintained that the spirits he believed in came in bottles. He had worked at the Monument Comb Shop since the age of fourteen; his booming laugh—or grumble—greeted us each night when he returned from the factory. A steady worker when the shop had enough work, he quickened with gaiety on Friday nights and weekends, a bottle of beer at his elbow, and he was fond of making long speeches about the good things in life. In the middle of the Depression, for instance, he paid cash for a piano, of all things, and insisted that my twin sisters, Yolande and Yvette, take lessons once a week.

I took a dime from my pocket and handed it to Armand.

"Thanks, Jerry," he said. "I hate to take your last cent."

---

caressed: touched gently and with affection
contempt: scorn; intense disapproval
gaiety: happiness; glee

"That's all right," I replied, turning away and consoling myself with the thought that twenty cents was better than nothing at all.

When I arrived at Lemire's I sensed disaster in the air. Roger Lussier was kicking disconsolately at a tin can in the gutter, and Rollie Tremaine sat sullenly on the steps in front of the store.

"Save your money," Roger said. He had known about my plans to splurge on the cards.

"What's the matter?" I asked.

"There's no more cowboy cards," Rollie Tremaine said. "The company's not making any more."

"They're going to have president cards," Roger said, his face twisting with disgust. He pointed to the store window. "Look!"

A placard in the window announced: "Attention, Boys. Watch for the New Series. Presidents of the United States. Free in Each 5-Cent Package of Caramel Chew."

"President cards?" I asked, dismayed.

I read on: "Collect a Complete Set and Receive an Official Imitation Major League Baseball Glove, Embossed with Lefty Grove's Autograph."

Glove or no glove, who could become excited about presidents, of all things?

Rollie Tremaine stared at the sign. "Benjamin Harrison, for crying out loud," he said. "Why would I want Benjamin Harrison when I've got twenty-two Ken Maynards?"

---

disconsolately: unhappily; gloomily
sullenly: in a glum, withdrawn, ill-tempered way
splurge: spend extra
embossed: decorated with a raised design, in this case a signature

I felt the warmth of guilt creep over me. I jingled the coins in my pocket, but the sound was hollow. No more Ken Maynards to buy.

"I'm going to buy a Mr. Goodbar," Rollie Tremaine decided.

I was without appetite, indifferent even to a Baby Ruth, which was my favorite. I thought of how I had betrayed Armand and, worst of all, my father.

"I'll see you after supper," I called over my shoulder to Roger as I hurried away toward home. I took the shortcut behind the church, although it involved leaping over a tall wooden fence, and I zigzagged recklessly through Mr. Thibodeau's garden, trying to outrace my guilt. I pounded up the steps and into the house, only to learn that Armand had already taken Yolande and Yvette uptown to shop for the birthday present.

I pedaled my bike furiously through the streets, ignoring the indignant horns of automobiles as I sliced through the traffic. Finally I saw Armand and my sisters emerge from the Monument Men's Shop. My heart sank when I spied the long, slim package that Armand was holding.

"Did you buy the present yet?" I asked, although I knew it was too late.

"Just now. A blue tie," Armand said. "What's the matter?"

"Nothing," I replied, my chest hurting.

He looked at me for a long moment. At first his eyes were hard, but then they softened. He smiled at me, almost sadly, and touched my arm. I turned away from him because I felt naked and exposed.

"It's all right," he said gently. "Maybe you've learned something." The words were gentle, but they held a curious dignity, the dignity remaining even when his voice suddenly cracked on the last syllable.

---

indignant: angry in response to something perceived as wrong

I wondered what was happening to me, because I did not know whether to laugh or cry.

Sister Angela was amazed when, a week before Christmas vacation, everybody in the class submitted a history essay worthy of a high mark—in some cases as high as A-minus. (Sister Angela did not believe that anyone in the world ever deserved an A.) She never learned—or at least she never let on that she knew—we all had become experts on the presidents because of the cards we purchased at Lemire's. Each card contained a picture of a president, and on the reverse side, a summary of his career. We looked at those cards so often that the biographies imprinted themselves on our minds without effort. Even our street-corner conversations were filled with such information as the fact that James Madison was called "The Father of the Constitution," or that John Adams had intended to become a minister.

The president cards were a roaring success and the cowboy cards were quickly forgotten. In the first place we did not receive gum with the cards, but a kind of chewy caramel. The caramel could be tucked into a corner of your mouth, bulging your cheek in much the same manner as wads of tobacco bulged the mouths of baseball stars. In the second place the competition for collecting the cards was fierce and frustrating—fierce because everyone was intent on being the first to send away for a baseball glove and frustrating because although there were only thirty-two presidents, including Franklin Delano Roosevelt, the variety at Lemire's was at a minimum. When the deliveryman left the boxes of cards at the store each Monday, we often discovered that one entire box was devoted to a single president—two weeks in a row the boxes contained nothing but Abraham

Lincolns. One week Roger Lussier and I were the heroes of Frenchtown. We journeyed on our bicycles to the North Side, engaged three boys in a matching bout and returned with five new presidents, including Chester Alan Arthur, who up to that time had been missing.

Perhaps to sharpen our desire, the card company sent a sample glove to Mr. Lemire, and it dangled, orange and sleek, in the window. I was half sick with longing, thinking of my old glove at home, which I had inherited from Armand. But Rollie Tremaine's desire for the glove outdistanced my own. He even got Mr. Lemire to agree to give the glove in the window to the first person to get a complete set of cards, so that precious time wouldn't be wasted waiting for the postman.

We were delighted at Rollie Tremaine's frustration, especially since he was only a substitute player for the Tigers. Once after spending fifty cents on cards—all of which turned out to be Calvin Coolidge—he threw them to the ground, pulled some dollar bills out of his pocket and said, "The heck with it. I'm going to buy a glove!"

"Not that glove," Roger Lussier said. "Not a glove with Lefty Grove's autograph. Look what it says at the bottom of the sign."

We all looked, although we knew the words by heart: "This Glove Is Not For Sale Anywhere."

Rollie Tremaine scrambled to pick up the cards from the sidewalk, pouting more than ever. After that he was quietly obsessed with the presidents, hugging the cards close to his chest and refusing to tell us how many more he needed to complete his set.

---

sleek: smooth and shiny
obsessed: very focused on, to the point of being unable to think about
  anything else

I too was obsessed with the cards, because they had become things of comfort in a world that had suddenly grown dismal. After Christmas a layoff at the shop had thrown my father out of work. He received no paycheck for four weeks, and the only income we had was from Armand's after-school job at the Blue and White Grocery Store—a job he lost finally when business dwindled as the layoff continued.

Although we had enough food and clothing—my father's credit had always been good, a matter of pride with him—the inactivity made my father restless and irritable. He did not drink any beer at all, and laughed loudly, but not convincingly, after gulping down a glass of water and saying, "Lent came early this year." The twins fell sick and went to the hospital to have their tonsils removed. My father was confident that he would return to work eventually and pay off his debts, but he seemed to age before our eyes.

When orders again were received at the comb shop and he returned to work, another disaster occurred, although I was the only one aware of it. Armand fell in love.

I discovered his situation by accident, when I happened to pick up a piece of paper that had fallen to the floor in the bedroom he and I shared. I frowned at the paper, puzzled.

"Dear Sally, When I look into your eyes the world stands still..."

The letter was snatched from my hands before I finished reading it.

"What's the big idea, snooping around?" Armand asked, his face crimson. "Can't a guy have any privacy?"

---

dismal: gloomy; bleak; sad
layoff: a situation when employees are released from their jobs, usually
    for a limited time
dwindled: decreased; lessened
crimson: deep red

He had never mentioned privacy before. "It was on the floor," I said. "I didn't know it was a letter. Who's Sally?"

He flung himself across the bed. "You tell anybody and I'll muckalize you," he threatened. "Sally Knowlton."

Nobody in Frenchtown had a name like Knowlton.

"A girl from the North Side?" I asked, incredulous. He rolled over and faced me, anger in his eyes, and a kind of despair, too.

"What's the matter with that? Think she's too good for me?" he asked. "I'm warning you, Jerry, if you tell anybody…"

"Don't worry," I said. Love had no particular place in my life; it seemed an unnecessary waste of time. And a girl from the North Side was so remote that for all practical purposes she did not exist. But I was curious. "What are you writing her a letter for? Did she leave town, or something?"

"She hasn't left town," he answered. "I wasn't going to send it. I just felt like writing to her."

I was glad that I had never become involved with love—love that brought desperation to your eyes, that caused you to write letters you did not plan to send. Shrugging with indifference, I began to search in the closet for the old baseball glove. I found it on the shelf, under some old sneakers. The webbing was torn and the padding gone. I thought of the sting I would feel when a sharp grounder slapped into the glove, and I winced.

"You tell anybody about me and Sally and I'll—"

"I know. You'll muckalize me."

I did not divulge his secret and often shared his agony, particularly when he sat at the supper table and left my

muckalize: a made-up word meaning "make into muck or mud"
incredulous: unable to believe
remote: distant; far away
winced: flinched; made a pained expression
divulge: to tell; to reveal

mother's special butterscotch pie untouched. I had never realized before how terrible love could be. But my compassion was short-lived because I had other things to worry about: report cards due at Eastertime; the loss of income from old Mrs. Belander, who had gone to live with a daughter in Boston; and, of course, the presidents.

Because a stalemate had been reached, the president cards were the dominant force in our lives—mine, Roger Lussier's and Rollie Tremaine's. For three weeks, as the baseball season approached, each of us had a complete set—complete except for one president, Grover Cleveland. Each time a box of cards arrived at the store we hurriedly bought them (as hurriedly as our funds allowed) and tore off the wrappers, only to be confronted by James Monroe or Martin Van Buren or someone else. But never Grover Cleveland, never the man who had been the twenty-second and the twenty-fourth president of the United States. We argued about Grover Cleveland. Should he be placed between Chester Alan Arthur and Benjamin Harrison as the twenty-second president or did he belong between Benjamin Harrison and William McKinley as the twenty-fourth president? Was the card company playing fair? Roger Lussier brought up a horrifying possibility—did we need *two* Grover Clevelands to complete the set?

Indignant, we stormed Lemire's and protested to the harassed storeowner, who had long since vowed never to stock a new series. Muttering angrily, he searched his bills and receipts for a list of rules.

---

stalemate: point at which nothing further can be done because two sides
   cannot agree
dominant: most important; controlling
harassed: constantly bothered
vowed: promised

"All right," he announced. "Says here you only need one Grover Cleveland to finish the set. Now get out, all of you, unless you've got money to spend."

Outside the store, Rollie Tremaine picked up an empty tobacco tin and scaled it across the street. "Boy," he said. "I'd give five dollars for a Grover Cleveland."

When I returned home I found Armand sitting on the piazza steps, his chin in his hands. His mood of dejection mirrored my own, and I sat down beside him. We did not say anything for a while.

"Want to throw the ball around?" I asked.

He sighed, not bothering to answer.

"You sick?" I asked.

He stood up and hitched up his trousers, pulled at his ear and finally told me what the matter was—there was a big dance next week at the high school, the Spring Promenade, and Sally had asked him to be her escort.

I shook my head at the folly of love. "Well, what's so bad about that?"

"How can I take Sally to a fancy dance?" he asked desperately. "I'd have to buy her a corsage… And my shoes are practically falling apart. Pa's got too many worries now to buy me new shoes or give me money for flowers for a girl."

I nodded in sympathy. "Yeah," I said. "Look at me. Baseball time is almost here, and all I've got is that old glove. And no Grover Cleveland card yet…"

---

piazza: porch
dejection: deep sadness; gloom
escort: date or companion
folly: foolishness
corsage: flowers worn on the shoulder or wrist on a special occasion

"Grover Cleveland?" he asked. "They've got some of those up on the North Side. Some kid was telling me there's a store that's got them. He says they're looking for Warren G. Harding."

"Holy smoke!" I said. "I've got an extra Warren G. Harding!" Pure joy sang in my veins. I ran to my bicycle, swung into the seat—and found that the front tire was flat.

"I'll help you fix it," Armand said.

Within half an hour I was at the North Side Drugstore, where several boys were matching cards on the sidewalk. Silently but blissfully I shouted: President Grover Cleveland, here I come!

After Armand had left for the dance, all dressed up as if it were Sunday, the small green box containing the corsage under his arm, I sat on the railing of the piazza, letting my feet dangle. The neighborhood was quiet because the Frenchtown Tigers were at Daggett's Field, practicing for the first baseball game of the season.

I thought of Armand and the ridiculous expression on his face when he'd stood before the mirror in the bedroom. I'd avoided looking at his new black shoes. "Love," I muttered.

Spring had arrived in a sudden stampede of apple blossoms and fragrant breezes. Windows had been thrown open and dust mops had banged on the sills all day long as the women busied themselves with housecleaning. I was puzzled by my lethargy. Wasn't spring supposed to make everything bright and gay?

I turned at the sound of footsteps on the stairs. Roger Lussier greeted me with a sour face.

"I thought you were practicing with the Tigers," I said.

"Rollie Tremaine," he said. "I just couldn't stand him." He slammed his fist against the railing. "Jeez, why did he have to be the one to get a Grover Cleveland? You should see him showing off. He won't let anybody even touch that glove..."

I felt like Benedict Arnold and knew that I had to confess what I had done.

"Roger," I said, "I got a Grover Cleveland card up on the North Side. I sold it to Rollie Tremaine for five dollars."

lethargy: extreme drowsiness

"Are you crazy?" he asked.

"I needed that five dollars. It was an—an emergency."

"Boy!" he said, looking down at the ground and shaking his head. "What did you have to do a thing like that for?"

I watched him as he turned away and began walking down the stairs.

"Hey, Roger!" I called.

He squinted up at me as if I were a stranger, someone he'd never seen before.

"What?" he asked, his voice flat.

"I had to do it," I said. "Honest."

He didn't answer. He headed toward the fence, searching for the board we had loosened to give us a secret passage.

I thought of my father and Armand and Rollie Tremaine and Grover Cleveland and wished that I could go away someplace far away. But there was no place to go.

Roger found the loose slat in the fence and slipped through. I felt betrayed: weren't you supposed to feel good when you did something fine and noble?

A moment later two hands gripped the top of the fence and Roger's face appeared. "Was it a real emergency?" he yelled.

"A real one!" I called. "Something important!"

His face dropped from sight and his voice reached me across the yard: "All right."

"See you tomorrow!" I yelled.

I swung my legs over the railing again. The gathering dusk began to soften the sharp edges of the fence, the rooftops, the distant church steeple. I sat there a long time, waiting for the good feeling to come.

# RAYMOND'S RUN
*by Toni Cade Bambara*

I don't have much work to do around the house like some girls. My mother does that. And I don't have to earn my pocket money by hustling; George runs errands for the big boys and sells Christmas cards. And anything else that's got to get done, my father does. All I have to do in life is mind my brother Raymond, which is enough.

Sometimes I slip and say my little brother Raymond. But as any fool can see he's much bigger and he's older too. But a lot of people call him my little brother cause he needs looking after cause he's not quite right. And a lot of smart mouths got lots to say about that too, especially when George was minding him. But now, if anybody has anything to say to Raymond, anything to say about his big head, they have to come by me. And I don't play the dozens or believe in standing around with somebody in my face doing a lot of talking. I much rather just knock you down and take my chances even if I am a little girl with skinny arms and a squeaky voice, which is how I got the name Squeaky. And if things get too rough, I run. And as anybody can tell you, I'm the fastest thing on two feet.

There is no track meet that I don't win the first place medal. I used to win the twenty-yard dash when I was a little kid in kindergarten. Nowadays, it's the fifty-yard dash. And tomorrow I'm subject to run the quarter-meter relay all by myself and come in first, second, and third. The big kids call

mind: to look after; to take care of
play the dozens: to engage in an exchange of insults, teasing, or taunting

me Mercury cause I'm the swiftest thing in the neighborhood. Everybody knows that—except two people who know better, my father and me. He can beat me to Amsterdam Avenue with me having a two fire-hydrant headstart and him running with his hands in his pockets and whistling. But that's private information. Cause you can imagine some thirty-five-year-old man stuffing himself into PAL shorts to race little kids? So as far as everyone's concerned, I'm the fastest and that goes for Gretchen, too, who has put out the tale that she is going to win the first-place medal this year. Ridiculous. In the second place, she's got short legs. In the third place, she's got freckles. In the first place, no one can beat me and that's all there is to it.

I'm standing on the corner admiring the weather and about to take a stroll down Broadway so I can practice my breathing exercises, and I've got Raymond walking on the inside close to the buildings, cause he's subject to fits of fantasy and starts thinking he's a circus performer and that the curb is a tightrope strung high in the air. And sometimes after a rain he likes to step down off his tightrope right into the gutter and slosh around getting his shoes and cuffs wet. Then I get hit when I get home. Or sometimes if you don't watch him he'll dash across traffic to the island in the middle of Broadway and give the pigeons a fit. Then I have to go behind him apologizing to all the old people sitting around trying to get some sun and getting all upset with the pigeons fluttering around them, scattering their newspapers and upsetting the waxpaper lunches in their laps. So I keep Raymond on the inside of me, and he plays like he's driving a stage coach which is O.K. by me so long as he doesn't run

---

Mercury: in ancient Roman mythology, the messenger god,
   known for speed

me over or interrupt my breathing exercises, which I have to do on account of I'm serious about my running, and I don't care who knows it.

Now some people like to act like things come easy to them, won't let on that they practice. Not me. I'll high-prance down 34th Street like a rodeo pony to keep my knees strong even if it does get my mother uptight so that she walks ahead like she's not with me, don't know me, is all by herself on a shopping trip, and I am somebody else's crazy child. Now you take Cynthia Procter for instance. She's just the opposite. If there's a test tomorrow, she'll say something like, "Oh, I guess I'll play handball this afternoon and watch television tonight," just to let you know she ain't thinking about the test. Or like last week when she won the spelling bee for the millionth time, "A good thing you got 'receive,' Squeaky, cause I would have got it wrong. I completely forgot about the spelling bee." And she'll clutch the lace on her blouse like it was a narrow escape. Oh, brother. But of course when I pass her house on my early morning trots around the block, she is practicing the scales on the piano over and over and over and over. Then in music class she always lets herself get bumped around so she falls accidently on purpose onto the piano stool and is so surprised to find herself sitting there that she decides just for fun to try out the ole keys. And what do you know—Chopin's waltzes just spring out of her fingertips and she's the most surprised thing in the world. A regular prodigy. I could kill people like that. I stay up all

---

accidently: an intentional misspelling of *accidentally,* to capture
  the character's casual way of speaking
ole: old
Chopin: Polish composer and pianist of the 19th century, famed for
  his works for piano
prodigy: genius; someone with amazing ability

night studying the words for the spelling bee. And you can see me any time of day practicing running. I never walk if I can trot, and shame on Raymond if he can't keep up. But of course he does, cause if he hangs back someone's liable to walk up to him and get smart, or take his allowance from him, or ask him where he got that great big pumpkin head. People are so stupid sometimes.

So I'm strolling down Broadway breathing out and breathing in on counts of seven, which is my lucky number, and here comes Gretchen and her sidekicks: Mary Louise, who used to be a friend of mine when she first moved to Harlem from Baltimore and got beat up by everybody till I took up for her on account of her mother and my mother used to sing in the same choir when they were young girls, but people ain't grateful, so now she hangs out with the new girl Gretchen and talks about me like a dog; and Rosie, who is as fat as I am skinny and has a big mouth where Raymond is concerned and is too stupid to know that there is not a big deal of difference between herself and Raymond and that she can't afford to throw stones. So they are steady coming up Broadway and I see right away that it's going to be one of those Dodge City scenes cause the street ain't that big and they're close to the buildings just as we are. First I think I'll step into the candy store and look over the new comics and let them pass. But that's chicken and I've got a reputation to consider. So then I think I'll just walk straight on through them or even over them if necessary. But as they get to me, they slow down. I'm ready to fight, cause like I said I don't feature a whole lot of chit-chat, I much prefer to just knock you down right from the jump and save everybody a lotta precious time.

---

liable: likely

"You signing up for the May Day races?" smiles Mary Louise, only it's not a smile at all. A dumb question like that doesn't deserve an answer. Besides, there's just me and Gretchen standing there really, so no use wasting my breath talking to shadows.

"I don't think you're going to win this time," says Rosie, trying to signify with her hands on her hips all salty, completely forgetting that I have whupped her behind many times for less salt than that.

"I always win cause I'm the best," I say straight at Gretchen who is, as far as I'm concerned, the only one talking in this ventriloquist-dummy routine. Gretchen smiles, but it's not a smile, and I'm thinking that girls never really smile at each other because they don't know how and don't want to know how and there's probably no one to teach us how, cause grown-up girls don't know either. Then they all look at Raymond who has just brought his mule team to a standstill. And they're about to see what trouble they can get into through him.

"What grade you in now, Raymond?"

"You got anything to say to my brother, you say it to me, Mary Louise Williams of Raggedy Town, Baltimore."

"What are you, his mother?" sasses Rosie.

"That's right, Fatso. And the next word out of anybody and I'll be their mother too." So they just stand there and Gretchen shifts from one leg to the other and so do they. Then Gretchen puts her hands on her hips and is about to say something with her freckle-face self but doesn't. Then she

---

ventriloquist-dummy routine: a performance in which the ventriloquist, a person who speaks with little or no lip movement, makes it appear that the dummy, or puppet, is speaking

sasses: talks disrespectfully

walks around me looking me up and down but keeps walking up Broadway, and her sidekicks follow her. So me and Raymond smile at each other and he says, "Gidyap" to his team and I continue with my breathing exercises, strolling down Broadway toward the ice man on 145th with not a care in the world cause I am Miss Quicksilver herself.

I take my time getting to the park on May Day because the track meet is the last thing on the program. The biggest thing on the program is the May Pole dancing, which I can do without, thank you, even if my mother thinks it's a shame I don't take part and act like a girl for a change. You'd think my mother'd be grateful not to have to make me a white organdy dress with a big satin sash and buy me new white baby-doll shoes that can't be taken out of the box till the big day. You'd think she'd be glad her daughter ain't out there prancing around a May Pole getting the new clothes all dirty and sweaty and trying to act like a fairy or a flower or whatever you're supposed to be when you should be trying to be yourself, whatever that is, which is, as far as I am concerned, a poor Black girl who really can't afford to buy shoes and a new dress you only wear once a lifetime cause it won't fit next year.

I was once a strawberry in a Hansel and Gretel pageant when I was in nursery school and didn't have no better sense than to dance on tiptoe with my arms in a circle over my head doing umbrella steps and being a perfect fool just so my mother and father could come dressed up and clap. You'd think they'd know better than to encourage that kind of nonsense. I am not a strawberry. I do not dance on my toes. I run. That is what I am all about. So I always come late to the

---

organdy: a fine, stiff, almost see-through fabric

May Day program, just in time to get my number pinned on and lay in the grass till they announce the fifty-yard dash.

I put Raymond in the little swings, which is a tight squeeze this year and will be impossible next year. Then I look around for Mr. Pearson, who pins the numbers on. I'm really looking for Gretchen if you want to know the truth, but she's not around. The park is jam-packed. Parents in hats and corsages and breast pocket handkerchiefs peeking up. Kids in white dresses and light-blue suits. The parkees unfolding chairs and chasing the rowdy kids from Lenox as if they had no right to be there. The big guys with their caps on backwards, leaning against the fence swirling the basketballs on the tips of their fingers, waiting for all these crazy people to clear out the park so they can play. Most of the kids in my class are carrying bass drums and glockenspiels and flutes. You'd think they'd put in a few bongos or something for real like that.

Then here comes Mr. Pearson with his clipboard and his cards and pencils and whistles and safety pins and fifty million other things he's always dropping all over the place with his clumsy self. He sticks out in a crowd because he's on stilts. We used to call him Jack and the Beanstalk to get him mad. But I'm the only one that can outrun him and get away, and I'm too grown for that silliness now.

"Well, Squeaky," he says, checking my name off the list and handing me number seven and two pins. And I'm thinking he's got no right to call me Squeaky, if I can't call him Beanstalk.

"Hazel Elizabeth Deborah Parker," I correct him and tell him to write it down on his board.

---

parkees: slang for people who work or spend much time in the park
glockenspiels: instruments with metal bars, played with small, light
hammers

"Well, Hazel Elizabeth Deborah Parker, going to give someone else a break this year?" I squint at him real hard to see if he is seriously thinking I should lose the race on purpose just to give someone else a break. "Only six girls running this time," he continues, shaking his head sadly like it's my fault all of New York didn't turn out in sneakers. "That new girl should give you a run for your money." He looks around the park for Gretchen like a periscope in a submarine movie. "Wouldn't it be a nice gesture if you were… to ahhh…"

I give him such a look he couldn't finish putting that idea into words. Grownups got a lot of nerve sometimes. I pin number seven to myself and stomp away, I'm so burnt. And I go straight for the track and stretch out on the grass while the band winds up with "Oh, the Monkey Wrapped His Tail Around the Flag Pole," which my teacher calls by some other name. The man on the loudspeaker is calling everyone over to the track and I'm on my back looking at the sky, trying to pretend I'm in the country, but I can't, because even grass in the city feels hard as sidewalk, and there's just no pretending you are anywhere but in a "concrete jungle" as my grandfather says.

The twenty-yard dash takes all of two minutes cause most of the little kids don't know no better than to run off the track or run the wrong way or run smack into the fence and fall down and cry. One little kid, though, has got the good sense to run straight for the white ribbon up ahead so he wins. Then the second-graders line up for the thirty-yard dash and I don't even bother to turn my head to watch cause Raphael Perez always wins. He wins before he even begins

---

periscope: a tube-like instrument used to see things not in one's direct line of sight

by psyching the runners, telling them they're going to trip on their shoelaces and fall on their faces or lose their shorts or something, which he doesn't really have to do since he is very fast, almost as fast as I am. After that is the forty-yard dash which I use to run when I was in first grade. Raymond is hollering from the swings cause he knows I'm about to do my thing cause the man on the loudspeaker has just announced the fifty-yard dash, although he might just as well be giving a recipe for angel food cake cause you can hardly make out what he's sayin for the static. I get up and slip off my sweat pants and then I see Gretchen standing at the starting line, kicking her legs out like a pro. Then as I get into place I see that ole Raymond is on line on the other side of the fence, bending down with his fingers on the ground just like he knew what he was doing. I was going to yell at him but then I didn't. It burns up your energy to holler.

Every time, just before I take off in a race, I always feel like I'm in a dream, the kind of dream you have when you're sick with fever and feel all hot and weightless. I dream I'm flying over a sandy beach in the early morning sun, kissing the leaves of the trees as I fly by. And there's always the smell of apples, just like in the country when I was little and used to think I was a choo-choo train, running through the fields of corn and chugging up the hill to the orchard. And all the time I'm dreaming this, I get lighter and lighter until I'm flying over the beach again, getting blown through the sky like a feather that weighs nothing at all. But once I spread my fingers in the dirt and crouch over the Get on Your Mark, the dream goes and I am solid again and am telling myself, Squeaky you must win, you must win, you are the fastest thing in the world, you can even beat your father up

psyching: slang for "intimidating, scaring, tricking"

Amsterdam if you really try. And then I feel my weight coming back just behind my knees then down to my feet then into the earth and the pistol shot explodes in my blood and I am off and weightless again, flying past the other runners, my arms pumping up and down and the whole world is quiet except for the crunch as I zoom over the gravel in the track. I glance to my left and there is no one. To the right, a blurred Gretchen, who's got her chin jutting out as if it would win the race all by itself. And on the other side of the fence is Raymond with his arms down to his side and the palms tucked up behind him, running in his very own style, and it's the first time I ever saw that and I almost stop to watch my brother Raymond on his first run. But the white ribbon is bouncing toward me and I tear past it, racing into the distance till my feet with a mind of their own start digging up footfuls of dirt and brake me short. Then all the kids standing on the side pile on me, banging me on the back and slapping my head with their May Day programs, for I have won again and everybody on 151st Street can walk tall for another year.

"In first place..." the man on the loudspeaker is clear as a bell now. But then he pauses and the loudspeaker starts to whine. Then static. And I lean down to catch my breath and here comes Gretchen walking back, for she's overshot the finish line too, huffing and puffing with her hands on her hips taking it slow, breathing in steady time like a real pro and I sort of like her a little for the first time. "In first place—" and then three or four voices get all mixed up on the loudspeaker and I dig my sneaker into the grass and stare at Gretchen who's staring back, we both wondering just who did win. I can hear old Beanstalk arguing with the man on the loudspeaker and then a few others running their mouths about what the stopwatches say. Then I hear Raymond yanking at the fence to call me and I wave to shush him, but he keeps rattling the fence like a gorilla in a cage like in them gorilla movies, but then like a dancer or something he starts climbing up nice and easy but very fast. And it occurs to me, watching how smoothly he climbs hand over hand and remembering how he looked running with his arms down to his side and with the wind pulling his mouth back and his teeth showing and all, it occurred to me that Raymond would make a very fine runner. Doesn't he always keep up with me on my trots? And he surely knows how to breathe in counts of seven cause he's always doing it at the dinner table, which drives my brother George up the wall. And I'm smiling to beat the band cause if I've lost this race, or if me and Gretchen tied, or even if I've won, I can always retire as a runner and begin a whole new career as a coach with Raymond as my champion. After all, with a little more study I can beat Cynthia and her phony self at the spelling bee. And if I bugged my mother, I could get piano lessons and become a star. And I have a big rep as the baddest thing around. And I've got a roomful of ribbons and medals and awards. But what has Raymond got to call his own?

So I stand there with my new plans, laughing out loud by this time as Raymond jumps down from the fence and runs over with his teeth showing and his arms down to the side, which no one before him has quite mastered as a running style. And by the time he comes over I'm jumping up and down so glad to see him—my brother Raymond, a great runner in the family tradition. But of course everyone thinks I'm jumping up and down because the men on the

---

shush: quiet
rep: short for "reputation"
baddest: slang for "best"

loudspeaker have finally gotten themselves together and compared notes and are announcing "In first place—Miss Hazel Elizabeth Deborah Parker." (Dig that.) "In second place — Miss Gretchen P. Lewis." And I look over at Gretchen wondering what the "P" stands for. And I smile. Cause she's good, no doubt about it. Maybe she'd like to help me coach Raymond; she obviously is serious about running, as any fool can see. And she nods to congratulate me and then she smiles. And I smile. We stand there with this big smile of respect between us. It's about as real a smile as girls can do for each other, considering we don't practice real smiling every day, you know, cause maybe we too busy being flowers or fairies or strawberries instead of something honest and worthy of respect... you know... like being people.

# I HAVE TEN LEGS

*by Anna Swir*
*translated by Czeslaw Milosz and Leonard Nathan*

When I run
I laugh with my legs.

When I run
I swallow the world with my legs.

When I run
I have ten legs.
All my legs
shout.

I exist
only when running.

# BOY FLYING

*by Leslie Norris*

Flying,
    He saw the earth as a plate,
    As if there were no hills, as if houses
    Were only roofs, as if the trees
    Were only leaves that covered
    The treetops. He could see the shadows
    The clouds cast when they sailed over the fields,
    He could see the river like the silver track
    Left by a snail, and roads narrow as ribbons.

    He could not see Mickey French next door,
    In bed with a cold, nor his two sisters
    Playing "Happy Families" as they watched
    The television. He could not see his kitten.

Flying,
    He felt the air as solid as water
    When he spread his fingers against it.
    He felt it cool against his face, he felt
    His hair whipped. He felt weightless
    As if he were hollow, he felt the sun
    Enormously bright and warm on his back,
    He felt his eyes watering. He felt
    The small, moist drops the clouds held.

He could not feel the grass, he could not
Feel the rough stones of the garden wall.
He could not remember the harsh, dry bark
Of the apple tree against his knees.

Flying,
       He could hear the wind hissing, the note
Changed when he turned his head. He heard
His own voice when he sang. Very faintly,
He heard the school bus as it grumbled
Past the church, he thought he could hear
The voices of people as they shouted
In amazement when they saw him swoop and glide.

He could not hear the birds sing, nor the chalk
Squeak against the blackboard, nor the mower
As it whirred along, nor the clock tick.
He could not hear the bacon sizzle in the pan,
He could not hear his friend calling him.

# THE BAT-POET
*by Randall Jarrell*

Once upon a time there was a bat—a little light brown bat, the color of coffee with cream in it. He looked like a furry mouse with wings. When I'd go in and out of my front door, in the daytime, I'd look up over my head and see him hanging upside down from the roof of the porch. He and the others hung there in a bunch, all snuggled together with their wings folded, fast asleep. Sometimes one of them would wake up for a minute and get in a more comfortable position, and then the others would wiggle around in their sleep till they'd get more comfortable too; when they all moved it looked as if a fur wave went over them. At night they'd fly up and down, around and around, and catch insects and eat them; on a rainy night, though, they'd stay snuggled together just as though it were still day. If you pointed a flashlight at them you'd see them screw up their faces to keep the light out of their eyes.

Toward the end of summer all the bats except the little brown one began sleeping in the barn. He missed them, and tried to get them to come back and sleep on the porch with him. "What do you want to sleep in the barn for?" he asked them.

"We don't know," the others said. "What do you want to sleep on the porch for?"

"It's where we always sleep," he said. "If I slept in the barn I'd be homesick. Do come back and sleep with me!" But they wouldn't.

So he had to sleep all
alone. He missed the
others. They had always
felt so warm and furry
against him; whenever
he'd waked, he'd
pushed himself up into
the middle of them and
gone right back to sleep.
Now he'd wake up and,
instead of snuggling
against the others and
going back to sleep, he

would just hang there and think. Sometimes he would open
his eyes a little and look out into the sunlight. It gave him a
queer feeling for it to be daytime and for him to be hanging
there looking; he felt the way you would feel if you woke up
and went to the window and stayed there for hours, looking
out into the moonlight.

It was different in the daytime. The squirrels and the
chipmunk, that he had never seen before—at night they were
curled up in their nests or holes, fast asleep—ate nuts and
acorns and seeds, and ran after each other playing. And all
the birds hopped and sang and flew; at night they had been
asleep, except for the mockingbird. The bat had always heard
the mockingbird. The mockingbird would sit on the highest
branch of a tree in the moonlight, and sing half the night. The
bat loved to listen to him. He could imitate all the other
birds—he'd even imitate the way the squirrels chattered
when they were angry, like two rocks being knocked
together; and he could imitate the milk bottles being put
down on the porch and the barn door closing, a long, rusty

squeak. And he made up songs and words all his own, that nobody else had ever said or sung.

The bat told the other bats about all the things you could see and hear in the daytime. "You'd love them," he said. "The next time you wake up in the daytime, just keep your eyes open for a while and don't go back to sleep."

The other bats were sure they wouldn't like that. "We wish we didn't wake up at all," they said. "When you wake up in the daytime the light hurts your eyes—the thing to do is to close them and go right back to sleep. Day's to sleep in; as soon as it's night we'll open our eyes."

"But won't you even try it?" the little brown bat said. "Just for once, try it."

The bats all said: "No."

"But why not?" asked the little brown bat.

The bats said: "We don't know. We just don't want to."

"At least listen to the mockingbird. When you hear him it's just like the daytime."

The other bats said: "He sounds so queer. If only he squeaked or twittered—but he keeps shouting in that bass voice of his." They said this because the mockingbird's voice sounded terribly loud and deep to them; they always made little high twittering sounds themselves.

"Once you get used to it you'll like it," the little bat said. "Once you get used to it, it sounds wonderful."

bass: low or deep-sounding

"All right," said the others, "we'll try." But they were just being polite; they didn't try.

The little brown bat kept waking up in the daytime, and kept listening to the mockingbird, until one day he thought: "I could make up a song like the mockingbird's." But when he tried, his high notes were all high and his low notes were all high and the notes in between were all high: he couldn't make a tune. So he imitated the mockingbird's words instead. At first his words didn't go together—even the bat could see that they didn't sound a bit like the mockingbird's. But after a while some of them began to sound beautiful, so that the bat said to himself: "If you get the words right you don't need a tune."

The bat went over and over his words till he could say them off by heart. That night he said them to the other bats. "I've made the words like the mockingbird's," he told them, "so you can tell what it's like in the daytime." Then he said to them in a deep voice—he couldn't help imitating the mockingbird—his words about the daytime:

> At dawn, the sun shines like a million moons
> And all the shadows are as bright as moonlight.
> The birds begin to sing with all their might.
> The world awakens and forgets the night.
>
> The black-and-gray turns green-and-gold-and-blue.
> The squirrels begin to—

But when he'd got this far the other bats just couldn't keep quiet any longer.

"The sun hurts," said one. "It hurts like getting something in your eyes."

"That's right," said another. "And shadows are black—how can a shadow be bright?"

Another one said: "What's green-and-gold-and-blue? When you say things like that we don't know what you mean."

"And it's just not real," the first one said. "When the sun rises the world goes to sleep."

"But go on," said one of the others. "We didn't mean to interrupt you."

"No, we're sorry we interrupted you," all the others said. "Say us the rest."

But when the bat tried to say them the rest he couldn't remember a word. It was hard to say anything at all, but finally he said: "I—I—tomorrow I'll say you the rest." Then he flew back to the porch. There were lots of insects flying around the light, but he didn't catch a one; instead he flew to his rafter, hung there upside down with his wings folded, and after a while went to sleep.

But he kept on making poems like the mockingbird's—only now he didn't say them to the bats. One night he saw a mother possum, with all her little white baby possums holding tight to her, eating the fallen apples under the apple tree; one night an owl swooped down on him and came so close he'd have caught him if the bat hadn't flown into a hole in the old oak by the side of the house; and another time four squirrels spent the whole morning chasing each other up and down trees, across the lawn, and over the roof. He made up poems about them all. Sometimes the poem would make him think: "It's like the mockingbird! This time it's really like the mockingbird!" But sometimes the poem would seem so bad to him that he'd get discouraged and stop in the middle, and by the next day he'd have forgotten it.

rafter: a beam or board that supports a roof

When he would wake up in the daytime and hang there looking out at the colors of the world, he would say the poems over to himself. He wanted to say them to the other bats, but then he would remember what had happened when he'd said them before. There was nobody for him to say the poems to.

One day he thought: "I could say them to the mockingbird." It got to be a regular thought of his. It was a long time, though, before he really went to the mockingbird.

The mockingbird had bad days when he would try to drive everything out of the yard, no matter what it was. He always had a peremptory, authoritative look, as if he were more alive than anything else and wanted everything else to know it; on his bad days he'd dive on everything that came into the yard—on cats and dogs, even—and strike at them with his little sharp beak and sharp claws. On his good days he didn't pay so much attention to the world, but just sang.

The day the bat went to him the mockingbird was perched on the highest branch of the big willow by the porch, singing with all his might. He was a clear gray, with white bars across his wings that flashed when he flew; every part of him had a clear, quick, decided look about it. He was standing on tiptoe, singing and singing and singing; sometimes he'd spring up into the air. This time he was singing a song about mockingbirds.

The bat fluttered to the nearest branch, hung upside down from it, and listened; finally when the mockingbird stopped just for a moment he said in his little high voice: "It's beautiful, just beautiful!"

---

peremptory: overly proud; haughty
authoritative: commanding

"You like poetry?" asked the mockingbird. You could tell from the way he said it that he was surprised.

"I love it," said the bat. "I listen to you every night. Every day too. I—I—"

"It's the last poem I've composed," said the mockingbird. "It's called 'To a Mockingbird.'"

"It's wonderful," the bat said. "Wonderful! Of all the songs I ever heard you sing, it's the best."

This pleased the mockingbird—mockingbirds love to be told that their last song is the best. "I'll sing it for you again," the mockingbird offered.

"Oh, please do sing it again," said the bat, "I'd love to hear it again. Just love to! Only when you've finished could I—"

But the mockingbird had already started. He not only sang it again, he made up new parts, and sang them over and over and over; they were so beautiful that the bat forgot about his own poem and just listened. When the mockingbird had finished, the bat thought: "No, I just can't say him mine. Still, though—" He said to the mockingbird: "It's wonderful to get to hear you. I could listen to you forever."

"It's a pleasure to sing to such a responsive audience," said the mockingbird. "Anytime you'd like to hear it again just tell me."

The bat said: "Could—could—"

"Yes?" said the mockingbird.

The bat went on in a shy voice: "Do you suppose that I— that I could—"

---

composed: created; made up
responsive: interested; appreciative

The mockingbird said warmly: "That you could hear it again? Of course you can. I'll be delighted." And he sang it all over again. This time it was the best of all.

The bat told him so, and the mockingbird looked pleased but modest; it was easy for him to look pleased but hard for him to look modest, he was so full of himself. The bat asked him: "Do you suppose a bat could make poems like yours?"

"A *bat?*" the mockingbird said. But then he went on politely, "Well, I don't see why not. He couldn't sing them, of course—he simply doesn't have the range; but that's no reason he couldn't make them up. Why, I suppose for bats a bat's poems would be ideal."

The bat said: "Sometimes when I wake up in the daytime I make up poems. Could I—I wonder whether I could say you one of my poems?"

A queer look came over the mockingbird's face, but he said cordially: "I'd be delighted to hear one. Go right ahead." He settled himself on his branch with a listening expression.

The bat said:

> A shadow is floating through the moonlight
> Its wings don't make a sound.
> Its claws are long, its beak is bright.
> Its eyes try all the corners of the night.
>
> It calls and calls: all the air swells and heaves
> And washes up and down like water.
> The ear that listens to the owl believes
> In death. The bat beneath the eaves,

---

range: in music, the extent of pitches, from low to high, that one can
    sing or play
cordially: politely
eaves: the part of a roof that hangs over the edge of a building

The mouse beside the stone are still as death—
The owl's air washes them like water.
The owl goes back and forth inside the night,
And the night holds its breath.

When he'd finished his poem the bat waited for the
mockingbird to say something; he didn't know it, but he
was holding his breath.

"Why, I like it," said the mockingbird. "Technically
it's quite accomplished. The way you change the rhyme-
scheme's particularly effective."

The bat said: "It is?"

"Oh yes," said the mockingbird. "And it was clever of you
to have that last line two feet short."

The bat said blankly: "Two feet short?"

"It's two feet short," said the mockingbird a little
impatiently. "The next-to-the-last line's iambic pentameter,
and the last line's iambic trimeter."

The bat looked so bewildered that the mockingbird said in
a kind voice: "An iambic foot has one weak syllable and one
strong syllable; the weak one comes first. That last line of
yours has six syllables and the one before it has ten; when
you shorten the last line like that it gets the effect of the night
holding its breath."

"I didn't know that," the bat said. "I just made it like
holding your breath."

accomplished: well-done; skillful
rhyme-scheme: the pattern of a rhyme in a poem
feet: in poetry, units of stressed and unstressed syllables
iambic pentameter: in poetry, a set of ten syllables with alternating weak
    and strong syllables
iambic trimeter: in poetry, a set of six syllables with alternating weak and
    strong syllables
bewildered: completely confused

"To be sure, to be sure!" said the mockingbird. "I enjoyed your poem very much. When you've made up some more do come round and say me another."

The bat said that he would, and fluttered home to his rafter. Partly he felt very good—the mockingbird had liked his poem—and partly he felt just terrible. He thought: "Why, I might as well have said it to the bats. What do I care how many feet it has? The owl nearly kills me, and he says he likes the rhyme-scheme!" He hung there upside down, thinking bitterly. After a while he said to himself: "The trouble isn't making poems, the trouble's finding somebody that will listen to them."

Before he went to sleep he said his owl poem over to himself, and it seemed to him that it was exactly like the owl. "The *owl* would like it," he thought. "If only I could say it to the *owl!*"

And then he thought: "That's it! I can't say it to the owl, I don't dare get that near him; but if I made up a poem about the chipmunk I could say it to the chipmunk—he'd be interested." The bat got so excited his fur stood up straight and he felt warm all over. He thought: "I'll go to the chipmunk and say, 'If you'll give me six crickets I'll make a poem about you.' Really I'd do it for nothing; but they don't respect something if they get it for nothing. I'll say: 'For six crickets I'll do your portrait in verse.'"

The next day, at twilight, the bat flew to the chipmunk's hole. The chipmunk had dozens of holes, but the bat had noticed that there was one he liked best and always slept in. Before long the chipmunk ran up, his cheeks bulging.

"Hello," said the bat.

The instant he heard the bat the chipmunk froze; then he dived into his hole. "Wait! Wait!" the bat cried. But the chipmunk had disappeared. "Come back," the bat called. "I won't hurt you." But he had to talk for a long time before the chipmunk came back, and even then he just stuck the tip of his nose out of the hole.

The bat hardly knew how to begin, but he timidly said to the chipmunk, who listened timidly: "I thought of making this offer to—to the animals of the vicinity. You're the first one I've made it to."

The chipmunk didn't say anything. The bat gulped, and said quickly: "For only six crickets I'll do your portrait in verse."

The chipmunk said: "What are crickets?"

The bat felt discouraged. "I knew I might have to tell him about poems," he thought, "but I never thought I'd have to tell him about *crickets*." He explained: "They're little black things you see on the porch at night, by the light. They're awfully good. But that's all right about them; instead of crickets you could give me—well, this time you don't have to give me anything. It's a—an introductory offer."

The chipmunk said in a friendly voice: "I don't understand."

"I'll make you a poem about yourself," said the bat. "One just about you." He saw from the look in the chipmunk's eyes that the chipmunk didn't understand. The bat said: "I'll say you a poem about the owl, and then you'll see what it's like."

He said his poem and the chipmunk listened intently; when the poem was over the chipmunk gave a big shiver

---

vicinity: the surrounding area or region
intently: with sharply focused attention

and said, "It's terrible, just terrible! Is there really something like that at night?"

The bat said: "If it weren't for that hole in the oak he'd have got me."

The chipmunk said in a determined voice: "I'm going to bed earlier. Sometimes when there're lots of nuts I stay out till it's pretty dark; but believe me, I'm never going to again."

The bat said: "It's a pleasure to say a poem to—to such a responsive audience. Do you want me to start on the poem about you?"

The chipmunk said thoughtfully: "I don't have enough holes. It'd be awfully easy to dig some more holes."

"Shall I start on the poem about you?" asked the bat.

"All right," said the chipmunk. "But could you put in lots of holes? The first thing in the morning I'm going to dig myself another."

"I'll put in a lot," the bat promised. "Is there anything else you'd like to have in it?"

The chipmunk thought for a minute and said, "Well, nuts. And seeds—those big fat seeds they have in the feeder."

"All right," said the bat. "Tomorrow afternoon I'll be back. Or day after tomorrow—I don't really know how long it will take." He and the chipmunk said goodbye to each other and he fluttered home to the porch. As soon as he got comfortably settled he started to work on the poem about the chipmunk. But somehow he kept coming back to the poem about the owl, and what the chipmunk had said, and how he'd looked. "*He* didn't say any of that two-feet-short stuff!" The bat hung there upside down, trying to work on his new poem. He was happy.

When at last he'd finished the poem—it took him longer than he'd thought—he went looking for the chipmunk. It was a bright afternoon, and the sun blazed in the bat's eyes, so that everything looked blurred and golden. When he met the chipmunk hurrying down the path that ran past the old stump, he thought: "What a beautiful color he is! Why, the fur back on his tail's rosy, almost. And those lovely black and white stripes on his back!"

"Hello," he said.

"Hello," said the chipmunk. "Is it done yet?"

"All done," said the bat happily. "I'll say it to you. It's named 'The Chipmunk's Day.'"

The chipmunk said in a pleased voice: "My day." He sat there and listened while the bat said:

> In and out the bushes, up the ivy,
> Into the hole
> By the old oak stump, the chipmunk flashes.
> Up the pole.
>
> To the feeder full of seeds he dashes,
> Stuffs his cheeks.
> The chickadee and titmouse scold him.
> Down he streaks.
>
> Red as the leaves the wind blows off the maple,
> Red as a fox,
> Striped like a skunk, the chipmunk whistles
> Past the love seat, past the mailbox,
>
> Down the path,
> Home to his warm hole stuffed with sweet
> Things to eat.
> Neat and slight and shining, his front feet
>
> Curled at his breast, he sits there while the sun
> Stripes the red west
> With its last light: the chipmunk
> Dives to his rest.

When he'd finished, the bat asked: "Do you like it?"

For a moment the chipmunk didn't say anything, then he said in a surprised, pleased voice: "Say it again." The bat said it again. "When he'd finished, the chipmunk said: "Oh, it's *nice*. It all goes in and out, doesn't it?"

The bat was so pleased he didn't know what to say. "Am I really as red as that?" asked the chipmunk.

"Oh yes," the bat said.

"You put in the seeds and the hole and everything," exclaimed the chipmunk. "I didn't think you could. I thought you'd make me more like the owl." Then he said: "Say me the one about the owl."

The bat did. The chipmunk said: "It makes me shiver. Why do I like it if it makes me shiver?"

"I don't know. I see why the owl would like it, but I don't see why we like it."

"Who are you going to do now?" asked the chipmunk.

The bat said: "I don't know. I haven't thought about anybody but you. Maybe I could do a bird."

"Why don't you do the cardinal? He's red and black like me, and he eats seeds at the feeder like me—you'd be in practice."

The bat said doubtfully: "I've watched him, but I don't know him."

"I'll ask him," said the chipmunk. "I'll tell him what it's like, and then he's sure to want to."

"That's awfully nice of you," said the bat. "I'd love to do one about him. I like to watch him feed his babies."

The next day, while the bat was hanging from his rafter fast asleep, the chipmunk ran up the ivy to the porch and called to the bat: "He wants you to." The bat stirred a little and blinked his eyes, and the chipmunk said: "The cardinal wants you to. I had a hard time telling him what a poem was like, but after I did he wanted you to."

"All right," said the bat sleepily. "I'll start it tonight."

The chipmunk said: "What did you say I was as red as? I don't mean a fox. I remember that."

"As maple leaves. As leaves the wind blows off the maple."

"Oh yes, I remember now," the chipmunk said; he ran off contentedly.

When the bat woke up that night he thought, "Now I'll begin on the cardinal." He thought about how red the cardinal was, and how he sang, and what he ate, and how he fed his big brown babies. But somehow he couldn't get started.

All the next day he watched the cardinal. The bat hung from his rafter, a few feet from the feeder, and whenever the cardinal came to the feeder he'd stare at him and hope he'd get an idea. It was queer the way the cardinal cracked the sunflower seeds; instead of standing on them and hammering them open, like a titmouse, he'd turn them over and over in his beak—it gave him a thoughtful look—and all at once the seed would fall open, split in two. While the cardinal was cracking the seed his two babies stood underneath him on tiptoe, fluttering their wings and quivering all over, their mouths wide open. They were a beautiful soft bright brown—even their beaks were brown— and they were already as big as their father. Really they were old enough to feed themselves, and did whenever he wasn't there; but as long as he was there they begged and begged, till the father would fly down by one and stuff the seed in its mouth, while the other quivered and cheeped as if its heart were breaking. The father was such a beautiful clear bright red, with his tall crest the wind rippled like fur, that it didn't seem right for him to be so harried and useful and hard-working: it was like seeing a general in a red uniform washing hundreds and hundreds of dishes. The babies

---

quivering: shaking or trembling
crest: a tuft of hair on a bird's head
harried: bothered

followed him everywhere, and kept sticking their open mouths up by his mouth—they shook all over, they begged so hard—and he never got a bite for himself.

But it was no use: no matter how much the bat watched, he never got an idea. Finally he went to the chipmunk and said in a perplexed voice: "I can't make up a poem about the cardinal."

The chipmunk said: "Why, just say what he's like, the way you did with the owl and me."

"I would if I could," the bat said, "but I can't. I don't know why I can't, but I can't. I watch him and he's just beautiful, he'd make a beautiful poem; but I can't think of anything."

"That's *queer*," the chipmunk said.

The bat said in a discouraged voice: "I guess I can't make portraits of the animals after all."

"What a shame!"

"Oh well," the bat said, "it was just so I'd have somebody to say them to. Now that I've got you I'm all right—when I get a good idea I'll make a poem about it and say it to you."

"I'll tell the cardinal you couldn't," the chipmunk said. "He won't be too disappointed, he never has heard a poem. I tried to tell him what they're like, but I don't think he really understood."

He went off to tell the cardinal, and the bat flew home. He felt relieved; it was wonderful not to have to worry about the cardinal anymore.

All morning the mockingbird had been chasing everything out of the yard—he gave you the feeling that having anything else in the world was more than he could bear. Finally he flew up to the porch, sat on the arm of the chair, and began to chirp in a loud, impatient, demanding

---

perplexed: puzzled

way, until the lady who lived inside brought him out some raisins. He flew up to a branch, waited impatiently, and as soon as she was gone dived down on the raisins and ate up every one. Then he flew over the willow and began to sing with all his might.

The bat clung to his rafter, listening drowsily. Sometimes he would open his eyes a little, and the sunlight and the shadows and the red and yellow and orange branches waving in the wind made a kind of blurred pattern, so that he would blink, and let his eyelids steal together, and go contentedly back to sleep. When he woke up it was almost dark; the sunlight was gone, and the red and yellow and orange leaves were all gray, but the mockingbird was still singing.

The porch light was lit, and there were already dozens of insects circling round it. As the bat flew toward them he felt hungry but comfortable.

Just then the mockingbird began to imitate a jay—not the way a jay squawks or scolds but the way he really sings, in a deep soft voice; as he listened the bat remembered how the mockingbird had driven off two jays that morning. He thought: "It's queer the way he drives everything off and then imitates it. You wouldn't think that—"

And at that instant he had an idea for a poem. The insects were still flying round and round the light, the mockingbird was still imitating the jay, but the bat didn't eat and he didn't listen; he flapped slowly and thoughtfully back to his rafter and began to work on the poem.

When he finally finished it—he worked on it off and on for two nights—he flew off to find the chipmunk. "I've got a new one," he said happily.

---

drowsily: sleepily

"What's it about?"

"The mockingbird."

"The mockingbird!" the chipmunk repeated. "Say it to me."
He was sitting up with his paws on his chest, looking intently
at the bat—it was the way he always listened.

The bat said:

> Look one way and the sun is going down,
> Look the other and the moon is rising.
> The sparrow's shadow's longer than the lawn.
> The bats squeak: "Night is here," the birds cheep:
>     "Day is gone."
> On the willow's highest branch, monopolizing
> Day and night, cheeping, squeaking, soaring,
> The mockingbird is imitating life.
> All day the mockingbird has owned the yard.
> As light first woke the world, the sparrows trooped
> Onto the seedy lawn: the mockingbird
> Chased them off shrieking. Hour by hour, fighting hard
> To make the world his own, he swooped
> On thrushes, thrashers, jays, and chickadees—
> At noon he drove away a big black cat.
>
> Now, in the moonlight, he sits here and sings.
> A thrush is singing, then a thrasher, then a jay—
> Then, all at once, a cat begins meowing.
> A mockingbird can sound like anything.
> He imitates the world he drove away
> So well that for a minute, in the moonlight,
> Which one's the mockingbird? Which one's the world?

---

monopolizing: taking complete control over

When he had finished, the chipmunk didn't say anything; the bat said uneasily, "Did you like it?"

For a minute the chipmunk didn't answer him. Then he said: "It really is like him. You know, he's chased me. And can he imitate me! You wouldn't think he'd drive you away *and* imitate you. You wouldn't think he could."

The bat could see that what the chipmunk said meant that he liked the poem, but he couldn't keep from saying: "You do like it?"

The chipmunk said, "Yes, I like it. But he won't like it."

"You liked the one about you," the bat said.

"Yes," the chipmunk answered. "But he won't like the one about him."

The bat said: "But it *is* like him."

The chipmunk said: "Just like. Why don't you go say it to him? I'll go with you."

When they found the mockingbird—it was one of his good days—the bat told him that he had made up a new poem. "Could I say it to you?" he asked. He sounded timid—guilty almost.

"To be sure, to be sure!" answered the mockingbird, and put on his listening expression.

The bat said, "It's a poem about—well, about mockingbirds."

The mockingbird repeated: "About mockingbirds!" His face had changed, so that he had to look listening all over again. Then the bat repeated to the mockingbird his poem about the mockingbird. The mockingbird listened intently, staring at the bat; the chipmunk listened intently, staring at the mockingbird.

When the bat had finished, nobody said anything. Finally the chipmunk said: "Did it take you long to make it up?"

Before the bat could answer, the mockingbird exclaimed angrily: "You sound as if there were something wrong with imitating things!"

"Oh no," the bat said.

"Well then, you sound as if there were something wrong with driving them off. It's my territory, isn't it? If you can't drive things off your own territory what can you do?"

The bat didn't know what to say; after a minute the chipmunk said uneasily, "He just meant it's odd to drive them all off and then imitate them so well too."

territory: an area that an animal defends as its own

"Odd!" cried the mockingbird. "Odd! If I didn't it really would be odd. Did you ever hear of a mockingbird that didn't?"

The bat said politely: "No indeed. No, it's just what mockingbirds do do. That's really why I made up the poem about it—I admire mockingbirds so much, you know."

The chipmunk said: "He talks about them all the time."

"A mockingbird's *sensitive*," said the mockingbird; when he said *sensitive* his voice went way up and way back down. "They get on my nerves. You just don't understand how much they get on my nerves. Sometimes I think if I can't get rid of them I'll go crazy."

"If they didn't get on your nerves so, maybe you wouldn't be able to imitate them so well," the chipmunk said in a helpful, hopeful voice.

"And the way they sing!" cried the mockingbird. "One two three, one two three—the same thing, the same thing, always the same old thing! If only they'd just once sing something different!"

The bat said: "Yes, I can see how hard on you it must be. I meant for the poem to show that, but I'm afraid I must not have done it right."

"You just haven't any *idea!*" the mockingbird went on, his eyes flashing and his feathers standing up. "Nobody but a mockingbird has any *idea!*"

The bat and the chipmunk were looking at the mockingbird with the same impressed, uneasy look. From then on they were very careful what they said—mostly they just listened, while the mockingbird told them what it was like to be a mockingbird. Toward the end he seemed considerably calmer and more cheerful, and even told the bat he had enjoyed hearing his poem.

The bat looked pleased, and asked the mockingbird: "Did you like the way I rhymed the first lines of the stanzas and then didn't rhyme the last two?"

The mockingbird said shortly: "I didn't notice"; the chipmunk told the mockingbird how much he always enjoyed hearing the mockingbird sing; and, a little later, the bat and the chipmunk told the mockingbird goodbye.

When they had left, the two of them looked at each other and the bat said: "You were right."

"Yes," said the chipmunk. Then he said: "I'm glad I'm not a mockingbird."

"I'd like to be because of the poems," the bat said, "but as long as I'm not, I'm glad I'm not."

"He thinks that he's different from everything else," the chipmunk said, "and he is."

The bat said, just as if he hadn't heard the chipmunk: "I wish I could make up a poem about bats."

The chipmunk asked: "Why don't you?"

"If I had one about bats maybe I could say it to the bats."

"That's right."

For weeks he wished that he had the poem. He would hunt all night, and catch and eat hundreds and hundreds of gnats and moths and crickets, and all the time he would be thinking: "If only I could make up a poem about bats!" One day he dreamed that it was done and that he was saying it to them, but when he woke up all he could remember was the way it ended:

> At sunrise, suddenly the porch was bats:
> A thousand bats were hanging from the rafter.

It had sounded wonderful in his dream, but now it just made him wish that the bats still slept on the porch. He felt cold and lonely. Two squirrels had climbed up in the feeder and were making the same queer noise—a kind of whistling growl—to scare each other away; somewhere on the other side of the house the mockingbird was singing. The bat shut his eyes.

For some reason, he began to think of the first things he could remember. Till a bat is two weeks old he's never alone: the little naked thing—he hasn't even any fur—clings to his mother wherever she goes. After that she leaves him at night; and the other babies hang there sleeping, till at last their mothers come home to them. Sleepily, almost dreaming, the bat began to make up a poem about a mother and her baby.

It was easier than the other poems, somehow: all he had to do was remember what it had been like and every once in a while put in a rhyme. But easy as it was, he kept getting tired and going to sleep, and would forget parts and have to make them over. When at last he finished he went to say it to the chipmunk.

The trees were all bare, and the wind blew the leaves past the chipmunk's hole; it was cold. When the chipmunk stuck his head out it looked fatter than the bat had ever seen it. The chipmunk said in a slow, dazed voice: "It's all full. My hole's all full." Then he exclaimed surprised to the bat: "How fat you are!"

"I?" the bat asked. "I'm fat?" Then he realized it was so; for weeks he had been eating and eating and eating. He said: "I've done my poem about the bats. It's about a mother and her baby."

"Say it to me."

The bat said:

A bat is born
Naked and blind and pale.
His mother makes a pocket of her tail
And catches him. He clings to her long fur
By his thumbs and toes and teeth.
And then the mother dances through the night
Doubling and looping, soaring, somersaulting—
Her baby hangs on underneath.
All night, in happiness, she hunts and flies.
Her high sharp cries
Like shining needlepoints of sound
Go out into the night and, echoing back,
Tell her what they have touched.
She hears how far it is, how big it is,
Which way it's going:
She lives by hearing.
The mother eats the moths and gnats she catches
In full flight; in full flight
The mother drinks the water of the pond
She skims across. Her baby hangs on tight.
Her baby drinks the milk she makes him
In moonlight or starlight, in mid-air.
Their single shadow, printed on the moon
Or fluttering across the stars,
Whirls on all night; at daybreak
The tired mother flaps home to her rafter.
The others all are there.
They hang themselves up by their toes,
They wrap themselves in their brown wings.

skims: glides lightly

Bunches upside down, they sleep in air.
Their sharp ears, their sharp teeth, their quick
    sharp faces
Are dull and slow and mild.
All the bright day, as the mother sleeps,
She folds her wings about her sleeping child.

When the bat had finished, the chipmunk said: "It's all really so?"

"Why, of course," the bat said.

"And you do all that too? If you shut your eyes and make a noise you can hear where I am and which way I'm going?"

"Of course."

The chipmunk shook his head and said wonderingly: "You bats sleep all day and fly all night, and see with your ears, and sleep upside down, and eat while you're flying and drink while you're flying, and turn somersaults in mid-air with your baby hanging on, and—and—it's really queer."

The bat said: "Did you like the poem?"

"Oh, of course. Except I forgot it was a poem. I just kept thinking how queer it must be to be a bat."

The bat said: "No, it's not queer. It's wonderful to fly all night. And when you sleep all day with the others it feels wonderful."

The chipmunk yawned. "The end of it made me all sleepy," he said. "But I was already sleepy. I'm sleepy all the time now."

The bat thought, "Why, I am too." He said to the chipmunk: "Yes, it's winter. It's almost winter."

"You ought to say the poem to the other bats," the chipmunk said. "They'll like it just the way I liked the one about me."

"Really?"

"I'm sure of it. When it has all the things you do, you can't help liking it."

"Thank you so much for letting me say it to you," the bat said. "I will say it to them. I'll go say it to them now."

"Goodbye," said the chipmunk. "I'll see you soon. Just as soon as I wake up I'll see you."

"Goodbye," the bat said.

The chipmunk went back into his hole. It was strange to have him move so heavily, and to see his quick face so slow. The bat flew slowly off to the barn. In the west, over the gray hills, the sun was red: in a little while the bats would wake up and he could say them the poem.

High up under the roof, in the farthest corner of the barn, the bats were hanging upside down, wrapped in their brown wings. Except for one, they were fast asleep. The one the little brown bat lighted by was asleep; when he felt someone light by him he yawned, and screwed his face up, and snuggled closer to the others. "As soon as he wakes up I'll say it to him," the bat thought. "No, I'll wait till they're all awake." On the other side of him was the bat who was awake: that one gave a big yawn, snuggled closer to the others, and went back to sleep.

The bat said to himself sleepily: "I wish I'd said we sleep all winter. That would have been a good thing to have in." He yawned. He thought: "It's almost dark. As soon as it's dark they'll wake up and I'll say them the poem. The chipmunk said they'd love it." He began to say the poem over to himself; he said in a soft contented whisper,

> A bat is born
> Naked and blind and pale.
> His mother makes a pocket of her tail
> And catches him. He clings—he clings—

He tried to think of what came next, but he couldn't remember. It was about fur, but he couldn't remember the words that went with it. He went back to the beginning. He said,

> A bat is born
> Naked and blind—

but before he could get any further he thought: "I wish I'd said we sleep all winter." His eyes were closed; he yawned, and screwed his face up, and snuggled closer to the others.

# THE WHITE UMBRELLA
*by Gish Jen*

**W**hen I was twelve, my mother went to work without telling me or my little sister.

"Not that we need the second income." The lilt of her accent drifted from the kitchen up to the top of the stairs, where Mona and I were listening.

"No," said my father, in a barely audible voice. "Not like the Lee family."

The Lees were the only other Chinese family in town. I remembered how sorry my parents had felt for Mrs. Lee when she started waitressing downtown the year before; and so when my mother began coming home late, I didn't say anything, and tried to keep Mona from saying anything either.

"But why shouldn't I?" she argued. "Lots of people's mothers work."

"Those are American people," I said.

"So what do you think we are? I can do the Pledge of Allegiance with my eyes closed."

Nevertheless, she tried to be discreet; and if my mother wasn't home by 5:30, we would start cooking by ourselves, to make sure dinner would be on time. Mona would wash the vegetables and put on the rice; I would chop.

For weeks we wondered what kind of work she was doing. I imagined that she was selling perfume, testing dessert recipes for the local newspaper. Or maybe she was

---

lilt: a lively, musical flow
audible: able to be heard
discreet: quiet; not attracting attention

working for the florist. Now that she had learned to drive, she might be delivering boxes of roses to people.

"I don't think so," said Mona as we walked to our piano lesson after school. "She would've hit something by now."

A gust of wind littered the street with leaves.

"Maybe we better hurry up," she went on, looking at the sky. "It's going to pour."

"But we're too early." Her lesson didn't begin until 4:00, mine until 4:30, so we usually tried to walk as slowly as we could. "And anyway, those aren't the kind of clouds that rain. Those are cumulus clouds."

We arrived out of breath and wet.

"Oh, you poor, poor dears," said old Miss Crosman. "Why don't you call me the next time it's like this out? If your mother won't drive you, I can come pick you up."

"No, that's okay," I answered. Mona wrung her hair out on Miss Crosman's rug. "We just couldn't get the roof of our car to close, is all. We took it to the beach last summer and got sand in the mechanism." I pronounced this last word carefully, as if the credibility of my lie depended on its middle syllable. "It's never been the same." I thought for a second. "It's a convertible."

"Well then make yourselves at home." She exchanged looks with Eugenie Roberts, whose lesson we were interrupting. Eugenie smiled good-naturedly. "The towels are in the closet across from the bathroom."

Huddling at the end of Miss Crosman's nine-foot leatherette couch, Mona and I watched Eugenie play. She was

---

cumulus clouds: large, puffy, usually white clouds
mechanism: moving part of a machine
credibility: believability
leatherette: fake leather

a grade ahead of me and, according to school rumor, had a boyfriend in high school. I believed it. She had auburn hair, blue eyes, and, I noted with a particular pang, a pure white, folding umbrella.

"I can't see," whispered Mona.

"So clean your glasses."

"My glasses are clean. You're in the way."

I looked at her. "They look dirty to me."

"That's because your glasses are dirty."

Eugenie came bouncing to the end of her piece.

"Oh! Just stupendous!" Miss Crosman hugged her, then looked up as Eugenie's mother walked in. "Stupendous!" she said again. "Oh! Mrs. Roberts! Your daughter has a gift, a real gift. It's an honor to teach her."

Mrs. Roberts, radiant with pride, swept her daughter out of the room as if she were royalty, born to the piano bench. Watching the way Eugenie carried herself, I sat up, and concentrated so hard on sucking in my stomach that I did not realize until the Robertses were gone that Eugenie had left her umbrella. As Mona began to play, I jumped up and ran to the window, meaning to call to them—only to see their brake lights flash then fade at the stop sign at the corner. As if to allow them passage, the rain had let up; a quivering sun lit their way.

The umbrella glowed like a scepter on the blue carpet while Mona, slumping over the keyboard, managed to eke out a fair

---

pang: a sudden feeling of emotional pain or distress
stupendous: superb; excellent; wonderful
radiant: glowing
royalty: belonging to a family of kings and queens
scepter: a rod that a king or queen carries
eke out: to do with great difficulty

rendition of a catfight. At the end of the piece, Miss Crosman asked her to stand up.

"Stay right there," she said, then came back a minute later with a towel to cover the bench. "You must be cold," she continued. "Shall I call your mother and have her bring over some dry clothes?"

"No," answered Mona. "She won't come because she..."

"She's too busy," I broke in from the back of the room.

"I see." Miss Crosman sighed and shook her head a little. "Your glasses are filthy, honey," she said to Mona. "Shall I clean them for you?"

Sisterly embarrassment seized me. Why hadn't Mona wiped her lenses when I told her to? As she resumed abuse of the piano, I stared at the umbrella. I wanted to open it, twirl it around by its slender silver handle; I wanted to dangle it from my wrist on the way to school the way the other girls did. I wondered what Miss Crosman would say if I offered to bring it to Eugenie at school tomorrow. She would be impressed with my consideration for others; Eugenie would be pleased to have it back; and I would have possession of the umbrella for an entire night. I looked at it again, toying with the idea of asking for one for Christmas. I knew, however, how my mother would react.

"Things," she would say. "What's the matter with a raincoat? All you want is things, just like an American."

Sitting down for my lesson, I was careful to keep the towel under me and sit up straight.

"I'll bet you can't see a thing either," said Miss Crosman, reaching for my glasses. "And you can relax, you poor dear. This isn't a boot camp."

---

rendition: a performance
boot camp: a military camp in which new soldiers undergo very
    hard training

When Miss Crosman finally allowed me to start playing I played extra well, as well as I possibly could. See, I told her with my fingers. You don't have to feel sorry for me.

"That was wonderful," said Miss Crosman. "Oh! Just wonderful."

An entire constellation rose in my heart.

"And guess what," I announced proudly. "I have a surprise for you."

Then I played a second piece for her, a much more difficult one that she had not assigned.

"Oh! That was stupendous," she said without hugging me. "Stupendous! You are a genius, young lady. If your mother had started you younger, you'd be playing like Eugenie Roberts by now!"

I looked at the keyboard, wishing that I had still a third, even more difficult piece to play for her. I wanted to tell her that I was the school spelling bee champion, that I wasn't ticklish, that I could do karate.

"My mother is a concert pianist," I said.

She looked at me for a long moment, then finally, without saying anything, hugged me. I didn't say anything about bringing the umbrella to Eugenie at school.

The steps were dry when Mona and I sat down to wait for my mother.

"Do you want to wait inside?" Miss Crosman looked anxiously at the sky.

"No," I said. "Our mother will be here any minute."

"In a while," said Mona.

"Any minute," I said again, even though my mother had been at least twenty minutes late every week since she started working.

According to the church clock across the street we had been waiting twenty-five minutes when Miss Crosman came out again.

"Shall I give you ladies a ride home?"

"No," I said. "Our mother is coming any minute."

"Shall I at least give her a call and remind her you're here? Maybe she forgot about you."

"I don't think she forgot," said Mona.

"Shall I give her a call anyway? Just to be safe?"

"I bet she already left," I said. "How could she forget about us?"

Miss Crosman went in to call.

"There's no answer," she said, coming back out.

"See, she's on her way," I said.

"Are you sure you wouldn't like to come in?"

"No," said Mona.

"Yes," I said. I pointed at my sister. "She meant yes, too. She meant no, she wouldn't like to go in."

Miss Crosman looked at her watch. "It's 5:30 now, ladies. My pot roast will be coming out in fifteen minutes. Maybe you'd like to come in and have some then?"

"My mother's almost here," I said. "She's on her way."

We watched and watched the street. I tried to imagine what my mother was doing; I tried to imagine her writing messages in the sky, even though I knew she was afraid of planes. I watched as the branches of Miss Crosman's big willow tree started to sway; they had all been trimmed to exactly the same height off the ground, so that they looked beautiful, like hair in the wind.

It started to rain.

"Miss Crosman is coming out again," said Mona.

"Don't let her talk you into going inside," I whispered.

"Why not?"

"Because that would mean Mom isn't really coming any minute."

"But she isn't," said Mona. "She's working."

"Shhh! Miss Crosman is going to hear you."

"She's working! She's working! She's working!"

I put my hand over her mouth, but she licked it, and so I was wiping my hand on my wet dress when the front door opened.

"We're getting even wetter," said Mona right away. "Wetter and wetter."

"Shall we all go in?" Miss Crosman pulled Mona to her feet. "Before you young ladies catch pneumonia? You've been out here an hour already."

"We're freezing." Mona looked up at Miss Crosman. "Do you have any hot chocolate? We're going to catch pneumonia."

"I'm not going in," I said. "My mother's coming any minute."

"Come on," said Mona. "Use your noggin."

"Any minute."

"Come on, Mona," Miss Crosman opened the door. "Shall we get you inside first?"

"See you in the hospital," said Mona as she went in. "See you in the hospital with pneumonia."

I stared out into the empty street. The rain was pricking me all over; I was cold; I wanted to go inside. I wanted to be

---

noggin: head

able to let myself go inside. If Miss Crosman came out again, I decided, I would go in.

She came out with a blanket and the white umbrella.

I could not believe that I was actually holding the umbrella, opening it. It sprang up by itself as if it were alive, as if that were what it wanted to do—as if it belonged in my hands, above my head. I stared up at the network of silver spokes, then spun the umbrella around and around and around. It was so clean and white that it seemed to glow, to illuminate everything around it.

"It's beautiful," I said.

Miss Crosman sat down next to me, on one end of the blanket. I moved the umbrella over so that it covered that too. I could feel the rain on my left shoulder and shivered. She put her arm around me.

"You poor, poor dear."

I knew that I was in store for another bolt of sympathy, and braced myself by staring up into the umbrella.

"You know, I very much wanted to have children when I was younger," she continued.

"You did?"

She stared at me a minute. Her face looked dry and crusty, like day-old frosting.

"I did. But then I never got married."

I twirled the umbrella around again.

"This is the most beautiful umbrella I have ever seen," I said. "Ever, in my whole life."

"Do you have an umbrella?"

"No. But my mother's going to get me one just like this for Christmas."

---

illuminate: to light up

"Is she? I tell you what. You don't have to wait until Christmas. You can have this one."

"But this one belongs to Eugenie Roberts," I protested. "I have to give it back to her tomorrow in school."

"Who told you it belongs to Eugenie? It's not Eugenie's. It's mine. And now I'm giving it to you, so it's yours."

"It is?"

She hugged me tighter. "That's right. It's all yours."

"It's mine?" I didn't know what to say. "Mine?" Suddenly I was jumping up and down in the rain. "It's beautiful! Oh! It's beautiful!" I laughed.

Miss Crosman laughed, too, even though she was getting all wet.

"Thank you, Miss Crosman. Thank you very much. Thanks a zillion. It's beautiful. It's stupendous!"

"You're quite welcome," she said.

"Thank you," I said again, but that didn't seem like enough. Suddenly I knew just what she wanted to hear. "I wish you were my mother."

Right away I felt bad.

"You shouldn't say that," she said, but her face was opening into a huge smile as the lights of my mother's car cautiously turned the corner. I quickly collapsed the umbrella and put it up my skirt, holding onto it from the outside, through the material.

"Mona!" I shouted into the house. "Mona! Hurry up! Mom's here! I told you she was coming!"

Then I ran away from Miss Crosman, down to the curb. Mona came tearing up to my side as my mother neared the house. We both backed up a few feet, so that in case she went onto the curb, she wouldn't run us over.

"But why didn't you go inside with Mona!" my mother asked on the way home. She had taken off her own coat to put over me, and had the heat on high.

"She wasn't using her noggin," said Mona, next to me in the back seat.

"I should call next time," said my mother. "I just don't like to say where I am."

That was when she finally told us that she was working as a check-out clerk in the A&P. She was supposed to be on the day shift, but the other employees were unreliable, and her boss had promised her a promotion if she would stay until the evening shift filled in.

For a moment no one said anything. Even Mona seemed to find the revelation disappointing.

"A promotion already!" she said, finally.

I listened to the windshield wipers.

"You're so quiet." My mother looked at me in the rear-view mirror. "What's the matter?"

"I wish you would quit," I said after a moment.

She sighed. "The Chinese have a saying: one beam cannot hold the roof up."

"But Eugenie Roberts's father supports their family."

She signed once more. "Eugenie Roberts's father is Eugenie Roberts's father," she said.

As we entered the downtown area, Mona started leaning hard against me every time the car turned right, trying to push me over. Remembering what I had said to Miss

---

A&P: at one time, a common grocery store chain
promotion: advancement to a better job or higher position in a company
revelation: something revealed or made known, usually something
  surprising

Crosman, I tried to maneuver the umbrella under my leg so she wouldn't feel it.

"What's under your skirt?" Mona wanted to know as we came to a traffic light. My mother, watching us in the rear-view mirror again, rolled slowly to a stop.

"What's the matter?" she asked.

"There's something under her skirt?" said Mona, pulling at me. "Under her skirt?"

Meanwhile, a man crossing the street started to yell at us. "Who do you think you are, lady?" he said. "You're blocking the whole crosswalk."

We all froze. Other people walking by stopped to watch.

"Didn't you hear me?" he went on, starting to thump on the hood with his fist. "Don't you speak English?"

My mother began to back up, but the car behind us honked. Luckily, the light turned green right after that. She sighed in relief.

"What were you saying, Mona?" she asked.

We wouldn't have hit the car behind us that hard if he hadn't been moving, too, but as it was our car bucked violently, throwing us all first back and then forward.

"Uh oh," said Mona when we stopped. "Another accident."

I was relieved to have attention diverted from the umbrella. Then I noticed my mother's head, tilted back onto the seat. Her eyes were closed.

"Mom!" I screamed. "Mom! Wake up!"

She opened her eyes. "Please don't yell," she said. "Enough people are going to yell already."

---

maneuver: to move into a certain position
diverted: turned aside

"I thought you were dead," I said, starting to cry. "I thought you were dead."

She turned around, looked at me intently, then put her hand to my forehead.

"Sick," she confirmed. "Some kind of sick is giving you crazy ideas."

As the man from the car behind us started tapping on the window, I moved the umbrella away from my leg. Then Mona and my mother were getting out of the car. I got out after them; and while everyone else was inspecting the damage we'd done, I threw the umbrella down a sewer.

# The Courage That
# My Mother Had

*by Edna St. Vincent Millay*

The courage that my mother had
Went with her, and is with her still:
Rock from New England quarried;
Now granite in a granite hill.

The golden brooch my mother wore
She left behind for me to wear;
I have no thing I treasure more:
Yet, it is something I could spare.

Oh, if instead she'd left to me
The thing she took into the grave!—
That courage like a rock, which she
Has no more need of, and I have.

---

quarried: removed from an open pit
granite: a very hard rock
brooch: a pin worn as jewelry, usually near the neck

# My Father Is a Simple Man

### by Luis Omar Salinas

I walk to town with my father
to buy a newspaper. He walks slower
than I do so I must slow up.
The street is filled with children.
We argue about the price
of pomegranates, I convince
him it is the fruit of scholars.
He has taken me on this journey
and it's been lifelong.
He's sure I'll be healthy
so long as I eat more oranges
and tells me the orange
has seeds and so is perpetual;
and we too will come back
like the orange trees.
I ask him what he thinks
about death and he says
he will gladly face it when
it comes but won't jump
out in front of a car.
I'd gladly give my life
for this man with a sixth
grade education, whose kindness

---

pomegranates: tart, juicy, red fruit with many seeds
scholars: learned people devoted to study
perpetual: ongoing; everlasting; continuing forever

and patience are true…
The truth of it is, he's the scholar,
and when the bitter-hard reality
comes at me like a punishing
evil stranger, I can always
remember that here was a man
who was a worker and provider,
who learned the simple facts
in life and lived by them,
who held no pretense.
And when he leaves without
benefit of fanfare or applause
I shall have learned what little
there is about greatness.

pretense: false appearance or intention
fanfare: a musical salute with trumpets; or, a showy public display

# THE LANGUAGE
# OF POETRY

# Nothing Gold Can Stay

*by Robert Frost*

Nature's first green is gold,
Her hardest hue to hold.
Her early leaf's a flower;
But only so an hour.
Then leaf subsides to leaf.
So Eden sank to grief,
So dawn goes down to day.
Nothing gold can stay.

---

hue: color; certain shade of a color
subsides: falls; settles downward
Eden: the biblical Garden of Eden; paradise

# A POISON TREE
### *by William Blake*

I was angry with my friend:
I told my wrath, my wrath did end.
I was angry with my foe:
I told it not, my wrath did grow.

And I water'd it in fears,
Night and morning with my tears:
And I sunned it with smiles,
And with soft deceitful wiles.

And it grew both day and night,
Till it bore an apple bright;
And my foe beheld it shine,
And he knew that it was mine,

And into my garden stole
When the night had veil'd the pole;
In the morning glad I see
My foe outstretch'd beneath the tree.

deceitful: dishonest; misleading
wiles: tricks intended to mislead or deceive
beheld: saw
veil'd: covered

# BEAUTY
### *by E-Yeh-Shure'*

Beauty is seen
In the sunlight,
The trees, the birds,
Corn growing and people working
Or dancing for their harvest.

Beauty is heard
In the night,
Wind sighing, rain falling,
Or a singer chanting
Anything in earnest.

Beauty is in yourself.
Good deeds, happy thoughts
That repeat themselves
In your dreams,
In your work,
And even in your rest.

---

in earnest: seriously and sincerely intended

# BARTER

*by Sara Teasdale*

Life has loveliness to sell,
    All beautiful and splendid things,
Blue waves whitened on a cliff,
    Soaring fire that sways and sings,
And children's faces looking up
Holding wonder like a cup.

Life has loveliness to sell,
    Music like a curve of gold,
Scent of pine trees in the rain,
    Eyes that love you, arms that hold,
And for your spirit's still delight,
Holy thoughts that star the night.

Spend all you have for loveliness,
    Buy it and never count the cost;
For one white singing hour of peace
    Count many a year of strife well lost,
And for a breath of ecstasy
Give all you have been, or could be.

---

strife: struggle; hard effort; conflict
ecstasy: intense emotion; overwhelming joy

# "ALL THE WORLD'S A STAGE"

*from* As You Like It, *Act 2: Scene 7*
*by William Shakespeare*

All the world's a stage,
And all the men and women merely players;
They have their exits and their entrances,
And one man in his time plays many parts,
His acts being seven ages. At first the infant,
Mewling and puking in the nurse's arms.
Then the whining schoolboy, with his satchel
And shining morning face, creeping like snail
Unwillingly to school. And then the lover,
Sighing like furnace, with a woeful ballad
Made to his mistress's eyebrow. Then a soldier,
Full of strange oaths, and bearded like the pard,
Jealous in honor, sudden, and quick in quarrel,
Seeking the bubble reputation
Even in the cannon's mouth. And then the justice,
In fair round belly with good capon lin'd,
With eyes severe and beard of formal cut,
Full of wise saws and modern instances;
And so he plays his part. The sixth age shifts
Into the lean and slipper'd pantaloon,

mewling: crying like a cat
satchel: a book bag
woeful: sad; full of grief
ballad: a song
pard: a leopard
capon: a neutered male chicken
pantaloon: pants

With spectacles on nose, and pouch on side,
His youthful hose, well sav'd, a world too wide
For his shrunk shank, and his big manly voice,
Turning again toward childish treble, pipes
And whistles in his sound. Last scene of all,
That ends this strange eventful history,
Is second childishness, and mere oblivion,
Sans teeth, sans eyes, sans taste, sans everything.

shank: lower leg
treble: a high-sounding voice
oblivion: a state of forgetfulness and lack of awareness
sans: without

# THREE POEMS
*by Emily Dickinson*

# THE WIND BEGAN TO ROCK THE GRASS

The Wind began to rock the Grass
With threatening Tunes and low –
He threw a Menace at the Earth –
A Menace at the Sky.

The Leaves unhooked themselves from Trees –
And started all abroad
The Dust did scoop itself like Hands
And threw away the Road.

The Wagons quickened on the Streets
The Thunder hurried slow –
The Lightning showed a Yellow Beak
And then a livid Claw.

The Birds put up the Bars to Nests –
The Cattle fled to Barns –
There came one drop of Giant Rain
And then as if the Hands

That held the Dams had parted hold
The Waters Wrecked the Sky
But overlooked my Father's House –
Just quartering a Tree –

menace: a threat
livid: very pale; very angry
quartering: dividing into four pieces

# I'll Tell You How the Sun Rose

I'll tell you how the Sun rose –
A Ribbon at a time –
The Steeples swam in Amethyst –
The news, like Squirrels, ran –

The Hills untied their Bonnets –
The Bobolinks – begun –
Then I said softly to myself –
"That must have been the Sun!"

But how he set – I know not –
There seemed a purple stile
That little Yellow boys and girls
Were climbing all the while –

Till when they reached the other side,
A Dominie in Gray –
Put gently up the evening Bars,
And led the flock away –

amethyst: a purple gem
bobolinks: a kind of bird
stile: steps that span across a wall or fence
Dominie: a clergyman, for example, a priest

# There Is No Frigate Like a Book

There is no Frigate like a Book
To take us Lands away
Nor any Coursers like a Page
Of prancing Poetry –
This Traverse may the poorest take
Without oppress of Toll –
How frugal is the Chariot
That bears the Human soul.

---

frigate: boat or ship
coursers: fast horses
traverse: a route; a way across
oppress: a burden
frugal: thrifty; inexpensive

# HARLEM [2]

*by Langston Hughes*

What happens to a dream deferred?

Does it dry up
like a raisin in the sun?
Or fester like a sore—
And then run?
Does it stink like rotten meat?
Or crust and sugar over—
like a syrupy sweet?

Maybe it just sags
like a heavy load.

*Or does it explode?*

deferred: put off; postponed
fester: to make pus; to rot

# HOLD FAST YOUR DREAMS
*by Louise Driscoll*

Hold fast your dreams!
Within your heart
Keep one still, secret spot
Where dreams may go,
And sheltered so,
May thrive and grow—
Where doubt and fear are not.
Oh, keep a place apart
Within your heart,
For little dreams to go.

# LIFE
*by James Russell Lowell*

Life is a leaf of paper white
Whereon each one of us may write
His word or two; and then comes night.

Though thou have time
But for a line, be that sublime;
Not failure, but low aim, is crime.

---

whereon: upon which
but for: for only
sublime: lofty; grand; inspiring awe and wonder

# ADVICE AND INSTRUCTION

# THE FISH I DIDN'T CATCH
*by John Greenleaf Whittier*

Our bachelor uncle who lived with us was a quiet, genial man, much given to hunting and fishing; and it was one of the pleasures of our young life to accompany him on his expeditions to Great Hill, Brandy-brow Woods, the Pond, and, best of all, to the Country Brook. We were quite willing to work hard in the cornfield or the haying lot to finish the necessary day's labor in season for an afternoon stroll through the woods and along the brookside.

I remember my first fishing excursion as if it were but yesterday. I have been happy many times in my life, but never more intensely so than when I received that first fishing pole from my uncle's hand, and trudged off with him through the woods and meadows. It was a still, sweet day of early summer; the long afternoon shadows of the trees lay cool across our path; the leaves seemed greener, the flowers brighter, the birds merrier, than ever before.

My uncle, who knew by long experience where were the best haunts of pickerel, considerately placed me at the most favorable point. I threw out my line as I had so often seen others, and waited anxiously for a bite, moving the bait in rapid jerks on the surface of the water in imitation of the leap of a frog. Nothing came of it. "Try again," said my uncle.

---

genial: friendly; kind
excursion: a trip
trudged: walked (usually with effort)
haunts: places often visited
pickerel: a small, freshwater fish

Suddenly the bait sank out of sight. "Now for it," thought I; "here is a fish at last."

I made a strong pull, and brought up a tangle of weeds. Again and again I cast out my line with aching arms, and

drew it back empty. I looked at my uncle appealingly. "Try once more," he said; "we fishermen must have patience."

Suddenly something tugged at my line, and swept off with it into deep water. Jerking it up, I saw a fine pickerel wriggling in the sun. "Uncle!" I cried, looking back in uncontrollable excitement, "I've got a fish!"

"Not yet," said my uncle. As he spoke there was splash in the water; I caught the arrowy gleam of a scared fish shooting into the middle of the stream—my hook hung empty from the line. I had lost my prize.

We are apt to speak of the sorrows of childhood as trifles in comparison with those of grown-up people; but we may depend upon it the young folks don't agree with us. Our griefs, modified and restrained by reason, experience, and self-respect, keep the proprieties, and, if possible, avoid a scene; but the sorrow of childhood, unreasoning and all-absorbing, is a complete abandonment to the passion. The doll's nose is broken, and the world breaks up with it; the marble rolls out of sight, and the solid globe rolls off with the marble.

So, overcome with my great and bitter disappointment, I sat down on the nearest hassock, and for a time refused to be comforted, even by my uncle's assurance that there were more fish in the brook. He refitted my bait, and, putting the pole again in my hands, told me to try my luck once more.

"But remember, boy," he said, with his shrewd smile, "never brag of catching a fish until he is on dry ground. I've seen older folks doing that in more ways than one, and so

---

arrowy: like an arrow
apt: likely
trifles: unimportant things
hassock: a tussock, that is, a thick clump of grass

making fools of themselves. It's no use to boast of anything until it's done, nor then, either, for it speaks for itself."

How often since I have been reminded of the fish that I did not catch. When I hear people boasting of a work as yet undone, and trying to anticipate the credit which belongs only to actual achievement, I call to mind that scene by the brookside, and the wise caution of my uncle in that particular instance takes the form of a proverb of universal application: "NEVER BRAG OF YOUR FISH BEFORE YOU CATCH HIM."

---

anticipate: to expect; to look forward to something as certain though it is
    yet to happen
proverb: a short, well-known saying containing a wise thought

# WORK
*by John Ruskin*

It is physically impossible for a well-educated, intellectual, or brave man to make money the chief object of his thoughts—as physically impossible as it is for him to make his dinner the principal object of them. All healthy people like their dinners, but their dinner is not the main object of their lives. So all healthily minded people like making money—ought to like it, and to enjoy the sensation of winning it; but the main object of their life is not money; it is something better than money.

A good soldier, for instance, mainly wishes to do his fighting well. He is glad of his pay—very properly so, and justly grumbles when you keep him ten years without it; still, his main notion of life is to win battles, not to be paid for winning them.

So of doctors. They like fees no doubt—ought to like them; yet if they are brave and well educated, the entire object of their lives is not fees. They, on the whole, desire to cure the sick; and—if they are good doctors, and the choice were fairly put to them—would rather cure their patient and lose their fee than kill him and get it. And so with all other brave and rightly trained men; their work is first, their fee second; very important always, but still *second*.

But in every nation, as I said, there are a vast class who are cowardly, and more or less stupid. And with these

---

object: purpose; goal
winning: gaining; earning

people, just as certainly the fee is first and the work second, as with brave people the work is first and the fee second.

And this is no small distinction. It is the whole distinction in a man. You cannot serve two masters; you *must* serve one or the other. If your work is first with you, and your fee second, work is your master.

Observe then, all wise work is mainly threefold in character. It is honest, useful, and cheerful. I hardly know anything more strange than that you recognize honesty in play, and you do not in work. In your lightest games you have always some one to see what you call "fair play." In boxing, you must hit fair; in racing, start fair. Your watchword is fair play; your hatred, foul play. Did it ever strike you that you wanted another watchword also, fair work, and another hatred also, foul work?

---

threefold: having three parts
watchword: motto; guiding principle

# HONEST WORK

**M**en said the old smith was foolishly careful, as he wrought on the great chain he was making in his dingy shop in the heart of the great city. But he heeded not their words, and only wrought with greater painstaking. Link after link he fashioned and welded and finished, and at last the great chain was completed.

Years passed. One night there was a terrible storm, and a ship was in sore peril of being dashed upon the rocks. Anchor after anchor was dropped, but none of them held. The cables were broken like threads.

At last the mighty sheet anchor was cast into the sea, and the old chain quickly uncoiled and ran out till it grew taut. All watched to see if it would bear the awful strain. It sang in the wild storm as the vessel's weight surged upon it. It was a moment of intense anxiety. The ship with its cargo of a thousand lives depended upon this one chain. What now if the old smith had wrought carelessly even one link of his chain!

But he had put honesty and truth and invincible strength into every part of it; and it stood the test, holding the ship in safety until the storm was over.

---

smith: blacksmith; one who forges iron
wrought: worked; shaped by hammering, cutting, and stretching
heeded not: paid no attention to
painstaking: careful work with great attention to detail
fashioned: shaped; formed
in sore peril: in extreme danger
sheet anchor: a large, strong anchor used only in emergencies
taut: tight; without any slack
invincible: unconquerable; incapable of being defeated

# FOR WANT OF A HORSESHOE NAIL

*adapted from James Baldwin*

*This is a legend about a real king, King Richard III of England,*
*who is generally regarded as one of England's worst rulers. In*
*1485, Richard was defeated in a battle against troops led by Henry,*
*Earl of Richmond. Many people remember the battle best because of*
*a line written by William Shakespeare in his play,* Richard III, *in*
*which Richard cries out, "A horse! A horse! My kingdom for a*
*horse!" Read on to understand the meaning of that desperate cry.*

The blacksmith paused from hammering the hot iron to
wipe his sweaty brow.

"Hurry up, man, hurry up!" cried a man at his side. "You
must shoe this horse quickly, for the king wishes to ride him
into battle!"

"Indeed, sir," said the blacksmith, "so you think there will
be a battle today?"

"Most certainly, and very soon, too," answered the man,
with an air of importance. "Why, when I left the field, the
king's enemies were on the march and ready for the fight.
Today will decide whether Richard or Henry shall rule
England. And as I am the king's groom, I charge you, sir,
make haste, for the king prefers this steed to all others!"

"As you say, sir," muttered the blacksmith as he bent back
to his tools, "though good work cannot be rushed."

From a bar of iron he made four horseshoes. Then he
hammered and shaped and fitted them to the horse's feet.

groom: one who looks after horses
charge: to command; to place a responsibility upon

Then he began to nail them on. But after he had nailed on two shoes, he found that he did not have enough nails for the other two.

"Begging your pardon, sir," he said to the impatient groom, "but as I've had to shoe so many horses these past few days, I now have only six nails left, and it will take a little time to hammer out the rest I need."

"You say you have six nails?" asked the groom with a stamp of his foot. "And only two shoes left to put on? Then put three nails in each shoe. That will have to do. Come, man, be quick about it. I think I hear the trumpets even now!"

The blacksmith cast him a doubtful look but did as he was told. He quickly finished the shoeing, and the groom hurried to lead the horse to the king.

The battle had been raging for some time. King Richard rode up and down the field, urging his men and slashing at his foes. His enemy, Henry, was pressing him hard.

Far away at the other side of the field, King Richard saw his men falling back in confusion. "Press forward! Press forward!" he yelled. Then he spurred his horse to ride toward the broken line and rally the men to turn and fight.

He was hardly halfway across the stony field when one of the horse's shoes flew off. A few steps more and another shoe came off. The horse stumbled, and King Richard was thrown to the ground.

Before the king could rise, his frightened horse had galloped away. The king looked up and saw that his soldiers were fleeing in confused retreat, and that on all sides Henry's troops were closing in upon him.

---

spurred: urged on and directed with spurs
rally: to rouse; to inspire toward a common purpose

He waved his sword in the air and shouted, "A horse! A horse! My kingdom for a horse!"

But there was no horse for him. His soldiers rushed past, intent on saving themselves.

The battle was lost. King Richard was lost. And Henry became king of England.

And since that time, people have said:

> *For want of a nail, the shoe was lost,*
> *For want of a shoe, the horse was lost,*
> *For want of a horse, the battle was lost,*
> *For want of a battle, the kingdom was lost,*
> *And all for the want of a horseshoe nail.*

---

intent: focused on some purpose

# ARGUMENT
*by Joseph Addison*

Avoid disputes as much as possible, in order to appear easy and well bred in conversation. You may assure yourself it requires more wit, as well as more good-humor, to improve rather than contradict the notions of another; but if you are at any time obliged to enter an argument, give your reasons with the utmost candor and modesty, two qualities which will scarcely ever fail to make an impression upon your hearers.

Besides, if you are not dogmatic, and if you do not show by your words or actions that you are self-conceited, all present will more heartily rejoice at your victory; nay, should you be worsted in argument, you may make your retreat with very good grace. You were never positive, and are now glad to be better informed.

In order to keep that good temper which is so difficult and yet so necessary to preserve, you should consider that nothing can be more unjust or ridiculous than to be angry with another because he is not of your opinion. The interests, education, and means by which men obtain their knowledge are so very different that it is impossible they should all think alike; and he has at least as much reason to be angry with you as you with him.

---

well bred: brought up well; raised properly
wit: intelligence
contradict: to express an opposite opinion
utmost: of the greatest or highest degree
candor: honesty and openness
dogmatic: pushy and overbearing in stating an opinion

Sometimes, to keep yourself cool, it may be of service to ask yourself fairly what would be your opinion if you had all the biases of education or interest your adversary may have. But if you contend for the honor of victory alone, you may lay down this as an infallible maxim, that you cannot make a falser step, or give your antagonist a greater advantage over you, than to fall into a passion.

When an argument is over, how many weighty reasons does a man recollect which his heat and violence made him utterly forget?

It is still more absurd to be angry with a man because he does not apprehend the force of your reasons, or gives weak ones of his own. If you argue for reputation, this makes your victory the easier; he is certainly, in all respects, an object of your pity rather than of your anger; and if he cannot comprehend your reasoning, you ought to thank nature for having given you so much the clearer understanding.

You may please to add this consideration: that among your equals no one values your anger, which only preys upon its master; and, perhaps, you may find it not very

biases: preferences that shape judgment; prejudices
adversary: an opponent; a challenger
contend: to strive; to struggle for
infallible: perfect; always correct
maxim: a short piece of wisdom; a truism
antagonist: an enemy; an adversary
fall into a passion: to lose control of one's emotions; to display intense and
    uncontrolled emotion, especially anger
absurd: completely unreasonable; ridiculous
apprehend: to understand
preys upon: injures; makes a victim of

consistent, either with prudence or with your ease, to punish yourself whenever you meet with a fool or a knave.

Lastly, if you propose to yourself the true end of argument, which is information, it may be a seasonable check to your passions; for if you search for truth only, it will be almost indifferent to you where you find it.

---

prudence: sound judgment; wisdom
knave: a tricky, dishonest person
seasonable: occurring in proper time
check: something that stops, holds back, or restrains
indifferent to: of no importance to; not mattering one way or another

# IF

*by Rudyard Kipling*

If you can keep your head when all about you
    Are losing theirs and blaming it on you;
If you can trust yourself when all men doubt you,
    But make allowance for their doubting too;
If you can wait and not be tired by waiting,
    Or, being lied about, don't deal in lies,
Or, being hated, don't give way to hating,
    And yet don't look too good, nor talk too wise;

If you can dream—and not make dreams your master;
    If you can think—and not make thoughts your aim;
If you can meet with triumph and disaster
    And treat those two impostors just the same;
If you can bear to hear the truth you've spoken
    Twisted by knaves to make a trap for fools,
Or watch the things you gave your life to broken,
    And stoop and build 'em up with worn-out tools;

If you can make one heap of all your winnings
    And risk it on one turn of pitch-and-toss,
And lose, and start again at your beginnings
    And never breathe a word about your loss;

---

make allowance for: to grant the possibility of
impostors: deceivers; persons who try to trick by assuming a false identity
knaves: tricky, dishonest people

If you can force your heart and nerve and sinew
  To serve your turn long after they are gone,
And so hold on when there is nothing in you
  Except the Will which says to them: "Hold on!"

If you can talk with crowds and keep your virtue,
  Or walk with kings—nor lose the common touch;
If neither foes nor loving friends can hurt you;
  If all men count with you, but none too much;
If you can fill the unforgiving minute
  With sixty seconds' worth of distance run—
Yours is the Earth and everything that's in it,
  And—which is more—you'll be a Man, my son!

---

sinew: muscle
virtue: goodness; moral strength

# CAN'T
### by Edgar Guest

*Can't* is the worst word that's written or spoken;
    Doing more harm here than slander and lies;
On it is many a strong spirit broken,
    And with it many a good purpose dies.
It springs from the lips of the thoughtless each morning
    And robs us of courage we need through the day:
It rings in our ears like a timely sent warning
    And laughs when we falter and fall by the way.

*Can't* is the father of feeble endeavor,
    The parent of terror and halfhearted work;
It weakens the efforts of artisans clever,
    And makes of the toiler an indolent shirk.
It poisons the soul of the man with a vision,
    It stifles in infancy many a plan;
It greets honest toiling with open derision
    And mocks at the hopes and the dreams of a man.

---

slander: false statements that damage a person's reputation
feeble: weak
endeavor: effort
artisans: artists and craftsmen
toiler: a worker
indolent: lazy
shirk: one who avoids work
stifles: smothers; holds back; suppresses
derision: ridicule; mockery
mocks at: ridicules; meanly makes fun of

*Can't* is a word none should speak without blushing;
    To utter it should be a symbol of shame;
Ambition and courage it daily is crushing;
    It blights a man's purpose and shortens his aim.
Despise it with all of your hatred of error;
    Refuse it the lodgment it seeks in your brain;
Arm against it as a creature of terror,
    And all that you dream of you someday shall gain.

*Can't* is the word that is foe to ambition
    An enemy ambushed to shatter your will;
Its prey is forever the man with a mission
    And bows but to courage and patience and skill.
Hate it, with hatred that's deep and undying,
    For once it is welcomed 'twill break any man;
Whatever the goal you are seeking, keep trying
    And answer this demon by saying: "I can."

---

ambition: strong desire to achieve
blights: ruins; destroys
lodgment: a place to stay
prey: hunted creature; victim
'twill: poetic shortened form of "it will"

# LETTER TO HIS SON
*by Robert E. Lee*

You must study to be frank with the world; frankness is the child of honesty and courage. Say just what you mean to do on every occasion and take it for granted you meant to do right. If a friend asks a favor, you should grant it if it is reasonable; if not, tell him plainly why you cannot; you will wrong him and wrong yourself by equivocation of any kind. Never do a wrong thing to make a friend or keep one; the man who requires you to do so is dearly purchased at a sacrifice. Deal kindly but firmly with all your classmates; you will find it the policy which wears best...

If you have any fault to find with anyone, tell him, not others, of what you complain; there is no more dangerous experiment than that of undertaking to be one thing before a man's face and another behind his back. We should live, act, and say nothing to the injury of anyone. It is not only best as a matter of principle but it is the path of peace and honor.

In regard to duty, let me, in conclusion of this hasty letter, inform you that nearly a hundred years ago there was a day of remarkable gloom and darkness—still known as "the dark day"—a day when the light of the sun was slowly extinguished as if by an eclipse. The Legislature of Connecticut was in session, and as the members saw the

---

study: to try hard
frank: candid; sincere
equivocation: misleading or deceptive language
dearly: at a very high price
policy: guiding principle; plan of action
hasty: hurried; quick

unexpected and unaccountable darkness coming on, they shared in the general awe and terror. It was supposed by many that the last day—the day of judgment—had come. Someone in the consternation of the hour moved an adjournment. Then there arose an old Puritan legislator, Davenport of Stamford, and said that if the last day had come he desired to be found in his place doing his duty and therefore moved that candles be brought in, so that the House could proceed with its duty. There was quietness in that man's mind, the quietness of heavenly wisdom and inflexible willingness to obey present duty.

Duty, then, is the sublimest word in our language. Do your duty in all things, like the old Puritan. You cannot do more, you should never wish to do less. Never let me and your mother wear one gray hair for any lack of duty on your part.

---

unaccountable: beyond any explanation; strange
awe: wonder; dread
consternation: state of confused amazement
adjournment: a break; the ending of an activity for a time
sublimest: greatest; most noble, admirable, and awe-inspiring

# MOTHER TO SON

*by Langston Hughes*

Well, son, I'll tell you:
Life for me ain't been no crystal stair.
It's had tacks in it,
And splinters,
And boards torn up,
And places with no carpet on the floor—
Bare.
But all the time
I'se been a-climbin' on,
And reachin' landin's,
And turnin' corners,
And sometimes goin' in the dark
Where there ain't been no light.
So boy, don't you turn back.
Don't you set down on the steps
'Cause you finds it's kinder hard.
Don't you fall now—
For I'se still goin', honey,
I'se still climbin',
And life for me ain't been no crystal stair.

---

landin's: landings, the level floors at the top or bottom of flights of stairs

# Perseverance

*by Johann Wolfgang von Goethe*

We must not hope to be mowers,
    And to gather the ripe gold ears,
Unless we have first been sowers
    And watered the furrows with tears.

It is not just as we take it,
    This mystical world of ours,
Life's field will yield as we make it
    A harvest of thorns or of flowers.

---

mowers: reapers; those who cut and gather the crop
sowers: those who plant seeds
furrows: the rows in a plowed field
mystical: having a hidden spiritual meaning
yield: to produce; to bear fruit

# THEY SHOULD HAVE LISTENED
## THREE CAUTIONARY TALES IN POETIC FORM

## REBECCA
### WHO SLAMMED DOORS FOR FUN AND PERISHED MISERABLY
*by Hilaire Belloc*

A Trick that everyone abhors
In Little Girls is slamming Doors.
A Wealthy Banker's Little Daughter
Who lived in Palace Green, Bayswater
(By name Rebecca Offendort),
Was given to this Furious Sport.

She would deliberately go
And Slam the door like Billy-Ho!
To make her Uncle Jacob start.
She was not really bad at heart,
But only rather rude and wild;
She was an aggravating child...

It happened that a Marble Bust
Of Abraham was standing just
Above the Door this little Lamb
Had carefully prepared to Slam,
And Down it came! It knocked her flat!
It laid her out! She looked like that.

---

abhors: hates
deliberately: purposefully; intentionally
aggravating: annoying
bust: a sculpture showing a person's head, neck, and shoulders

Her funeral Sermon (which was long
And followed by a Sacred Song)
Mentioned her Virtues, it is true,
But dwelt upon her Vices too,
And showed the Dreadful End of One
Who goes and slams the door for Fun.

The children who were brought to hear
The awful Tale from far and near
Were much impressed, and inly swore
They never more would slam the Door,
—As often they had done before.

---

inly: inwardly

# The Story of Augustus
## Who Would Not Have Any Soup
*by Heinrich Hoffmann*

Augustus was a chubby lad;
Fat, ruddy cheeks Augustus had;
And everybody saw with joy
The plump and hearty, healthy boy.
He ate and drank as he was told,
And never let his soup get cold.

But one day, one cold winter's day,
He screamed out—"Take the soup away!
O take the nasty soup away!
I won't have any soup today."

Next day begins his tale of woes;
Quite lank and lean Augustus grows.
Yet, though he feels so weak and ill,
The naughty fellow cries out still—

"Not any soup for me, I say:
O take the nasty soup away!
I won't have any soup today."

---

ruddy: rosy in color, as a sign of health
lank: thin

The third day comes: O what a sin!
To make himself so pale and thin.
Yet, when the soup is put on table,
He screams as loud as he is able—

"Not any soup for me, I say:
   O take the nasty soup away!
   I WON'T have any soup today."

Look at him, now the fourth day's come!
   He scarcely weighs a sugar-plum;
   He's like a little bit of thread,
   And on the fifth day, he was—dead!

sugar-plum: a small, ball-shaped candy

# SARAH CYNTHIA SYLVIA STOUT
## WOULD NOT TAKE THE GARBAGE OUT
### *by Shel Silverstein*

Sarah Cynthia Sylvia Stout
Would not take the garbage out!
She'd scour the pots and scrape the pans,
Candy the yams and spice the hams,
And though her daddy would scream and shout,
She simply would not take the garbage out.
And so it piled up to the ceilings:
Coffee grounds, potato peelings,
Brown bananas, rotten peas,
Chunks of sour cottage cheese.
It filled the can, it covered the floor,
It cracked the window and blocked the door
With bacon rinds and chicken bones,
Drippy ends of ice cream cones,
Prune pits, peach pits, orange peel,
Gloppy glumps of cold oatmeal,
Pizza crust and withered greens,
Soggy beans and tangerines,
Crusts of black burned buttered toast,
Grisly bits of beefy roasts...

---

candy: to cook in a heavy sugar syrup until glazed

The garbage rolled on down the hall,
It raised the roof, it broke the wall...
Greasy napkins, cookie crumbs,
Globs of gooey bubble gum,
Cellophane from green baloney,
Rubbery blubbery macaroni,
Peanut butter, caked and dry,
Curdled milk and crusts of pie,
Moldy melons, dried-up mustard,
Eggshells mixed with lemon custard,
Cold french fries and rancid meat,
Yellow lumps of Cream of Wheat.
At last the garbage reached so high
That finally it touched the sky.
And all the neighbors moved away,
And none of her friends would come to play.

---

rancid: spoiled; having a foul smell or taste
Cream of Wheat: a brand of breakfast porridge

And finally Sarah Cynthia Stout said,
"OK, I'll take the garbage out!"
But then, of course, it was too late...
The garbage reached across the state,
From New York to the Golden Gate.
And there, in the garbage she did hate,
Poor Sarah met an awful fate,
That I cannot right now relate
Because the hour is much too late.
But children, remember Sarah Stout
And always take the garbage out!

---

Golden Gate: the strait connecting the San Francisco Bay in California
  with the Pacific Ocean; also the name of the bridge that spans the strait

# INDEX OF AUTHORS AND TITLES

# ACKNOWLEDGMENTS

## Poems

"Beauty" by E-Yeh-Shure' from I AM A PUEBLO INDIAN GIRL by E-Yeh-Shure'. Copyright © 1936 by William Morrow and Company, Inc. Renewed 1967 by Louise Abieta Chiwiwi. Reprinted by permission of HarperCollins Publishers Inc.

"Boy Flying" by Leslie Norris from NORRIS'S ARK, Wells College Press, Aurora, N.Y.

"The Courage That My Mother Had" by Edna St. Vincent Millay from COLLECTED POEMS by Edna St. Vincent Millay, HarperCollins. Copyright © 1954, 1982 by Edna St. Vincent Millay and Norma Millay Ellis. All rights reserved. Reprinted by permission of Elizabeth Barnett, Literary Executor.

"Harlem [2]" and "Mother to Son" by Langston Hughes from THE COLLECTED POEMS OF LANGSTON HUGHES by Langston Hughes, copyright © 1994 by The Estate of Langston Hughes. Used by permission of Alfred A. Knopf, a division of Random House, Inc.; also, of Harold Ober Associates.

"I Have Ten Legs" by Anna Swir (translated by Czeslaw Milosz and Leonard Nathan). Copyright by Czeslaw Milosz. Reprinted by permission Leonard Nathan and on behalf of Mr. Milosz of Sterling Lord Literistic, Inc.

"The Listeners" by Walter de la Mare, reprinted by permission of the Literary Trustees of Walter de la Mare and the Society of Authors as their representative.

"My Father Is a Simple Man" by Luis Omar Salinas is reprinted with permission from the publisher of THE SADNESS OF DAYS, SELECTED AND NEW POEMS by Luis Omar Salinas (Houston: Arte Público Press—University of Houston, 1987).

"Nothing Gold Can Stay" and "Stopping by Woods on a Snowy Evening" from THE POETRY OF ROBERT FROST edited by Edward Connery Lathem. Copyright 1939, 1967, © 1969 by Henry Holt and Co. Reprinted by permission of Henry Holt and Company, LLC.

"Sara Cynthia Sylvia Stout Would Not Take the Garbage Out" by Shel Silverstein. Copyright © 1974 by Evil Eye Music, Inc.

"The White Umbrella" by Gish Jen, copyright © 1984 by Gish Jen. First published in *The Yale Review*. Reprinted by permission of the author.

## Stories

"Charles" by Shirley Jackson from THE LOTTERY AND OTHER STORIES by Shirley Jackson. Copyright © 1948, 1949 by Shirley Jackson. Copyright renewed 1976, 1977 by Laurence Hyman, Barry Hyman, Mrs. Sarah Webster and Mrs. Joanne Schnurer. Reprinted by permission of Farrar, Strauss, and Giroux, LLC.

"Michael Faraday's World" adapted from COILS, MAGNETS AND RINGS: MICHAEL FARADAY'S WORLD by Nancy Veglahn, copyright © by Nancy Veglahn, text. Used by permission of Coward-McCann, a division of Penguin Young Readers Group, A Member of Penguin Group (USA) Inc., 345 Hudson St., New York, NY 10014. All rights reserved.

## Illustrations